Let It Go Just Let It Go!

Let It Go Just Let It Go!

Kent A. Rader

Brown Books
Dallas

Let It Go—Just Let It Go!

Printed and bound in the United States of America

For information, please contact Brown Books
16200 North Dallas Parkway, Suite 225,
Dallas, Texas 75248
972-381-0009 www.brownbooks.com

First Printing, 2002

ISBN 0-9717162-0-X

LCCN 2002090589

For Twyla—

You are the love

of my life.

Acknowledgments

After hearing me speak for the first time, my dad told me I was the luckiest person he had ever met. He was right.

I would like to thank my parents for showing me that hard work and perseverance would always allow me to accomplish anything I set my mind to accomplishing. They somehow instilled me with the confidence that there wasn't anything I couldn't do, even when I got the harebrained idea to become a professional speaker and author. Thank you, Mom and Dad, for all you have done for me. I love you.

I want to thank Jim Stovall and Jeff Magee for sharing with me their knowledge and experience in speaking and writing. Their counsel has been priceless in helping me achieve my dream. Their unselfishness has taught me a valuable lesson which I will continue as I help speakers who join our ranks in the future.

Michael Johnson, one of the finest speakers and authors I have ever known, has given me so much. His friendship, his advice, his encouragement, and his love have been invaluable to my speaking career and to this book. He is one of the teachers who appeared when this student was ready to learn.

Milli Brown, Kathryn Grant, and others at Brown Books have been exceptional in making this project come to life. They have been patient, gentle, and kind enough not to laugh out loud at me. I appreciate all you have done for me and look forward to working together in the future.

I owe a great debt to the professors and administration of William Jewell College in Liberty, Missouri. I received a quality education in my chosen field of accounting, but more importantly, they had high expectations of me as a person. No wonder they were chosen *Time* magazine's number-one liberal arts college in the country for 2001.

I want to thank all the organizations who have hired me over the past four years to share my message. I love you all and hope to see you again on the road of life. Remember to take care of yourself and each other.

My friend, Mona Chapman, has been a godsend throughout this project. We have coffee together most of the mornings I am home. Over the past year many of these times together have been filled with my rumblings about parts of this text that are giving me difficulty. Mona always listens with a nonjudgmental ear and offers me advice that is sound and caring. She also laughs every time I read to her from Drew Carey's book *Dirty Jokes and Beer*, no matter how many times she has heard it. I love you, Mona.

My children, Keith and Maggie, have always been a source of joy, comfort, inspiration, and a wealth of great stories. They have never resented my sharing with the world many of the intimate moments of our family's life. They constantly motivate me to improve as a human being because they set the standard for honesty, humor, and love. Thank you both for being yourself. I hope I always make you proud.

Last, but certainly not least, I thank my wife Twyla for her support, not just on this project, but for every day of our marriage. I have rarely been easy to live with, these many years; yet, in spite of all of the problems, you are still here. You have been the most influential person in my life for without you, little I do would have meaning. I offer you my life and am looking forward to growing old with you.

Kent A. Rader

Let It Go—Just Let It Go!

Contents

Let It Go—Just Let It Go!

Chapter 1

Let It Go—Just Let It Go!

Yesterday, as my workday began, my computer made a very different and apparently bad noise as it started up. I called the local computer shop and asked what the problem may be. He said it sounded like my hard drive had gone out. I asked if my database for my speaking business might be lost. My hope was, through some sort of miracle of modern technology, he might be able to save it. He said probably not, but if it was brought in immediately, he could look at it.

The computer tower was packed into the car and driven to downtown Mangum, Oklahoma. It was my hope this computer failure would not be a disastrous situation because backing up my data is not one of my strongest computer skills. As I entered the store, I was fuming! I explained my hatred for these things. My experience with computers has not been good, as mine always seem to be lemons. My name-brand computer, purchased four years ago, crashed, losing all my information in the process. I decided to purchase another computer from a local vendor after that problem, as I thought the service would be better. My tirade proceeded by my telling him how the previous Christmas this same computer had crashed, again losing some of my information and causing me to do without it for a couple of weeks, while I took it to Oklahoma City to find someone to work on it because the local dealer had gone out of business! Now, just when I get this extensive database developed, it was potentially lost! "I HATE THESE THINGS!" I screamed in frustration.

Of course, this isn't verbatim, as there were words interspersed in this conversation that would make a sailor blush! (I think it was appropriate that this less than G-rated conversation took place on my Grandfather Rowan's 100th birthday, as he liked to use these poolhall words in his daily conversation, much to the dismay of my grandmother!) As I continued to tell the technician about the problems I had experienced with modern technology, he quietly hooked up the computer to his monitor, mouse, and keyboard. Just before he turned it on, he looked at me and simply asked if I had backed up my database. He said if the hard drive was bad, they could put a new one into the computer and reinstall the backup. I quietly told him I had not taken the time to back up this very important component to my speaking business. He looked at me and simply said, "Modern technology is wonderful, but it still needs humans to take the precautions that will make these problems less catastrophic!"

While feelings of inadequacy began to take hold of me, he started the computer. Much to my delight, the noise was gone and everything started up fine! I was very relieved that we would probably be able to save my database before the necessary repairs would be completed. With my new found commitment to always back up my work and maintain duplicate copies of everything, the technician began his work. Maybe he was thinking it was now safe to carry on a conversation with this person who just a few minutes before had been ranting like a madman. He asked me what I did for a living. I told him I was a professional speaker. He then asked the fatal question of this situation: "So what do you speak about?" I heard him say. Instantly, before recognizing the irony, I said, "Stress reduction!"

He gave me a look that I have seen only from my mom when I told her, at the age of eleven, that the mirror in the bathroom had exploded and I didn't know how it happened. (The truth was I had hit it with my elbow, practicing football moves. I wanted to see how tough I looked when I delivered the block that would spring Ed Podolak into the open for the game-winning touchdown for the Kansas City Chiefs!) He finally asked, "Is this the behavior that you teach in your classes?"

Yes, stress happens to us all! The thing about stress is that there are different stimuli that cause the feelings of stress. We will discuss this more later in the book, but for now, let us examine why stress is so prevalent in our society today!

In examining the reasons why stress is so common to everyone today, one only needs to look at how today's society is vastly different from what it was thirty to forty years ago. Not only has the nature of business changed, but our society's family unit has changed. Today, most people involved in a relationship are probably involved in a dual-income family! Forty years ago, most families had one adult as the breadwinner, holding down the responsibilities of a career and providing the family with their source of income! The other adult in the relationship maintained the home and the burdens associated with it. This included, but wasn't limited to, cooking meals, rearing children, cleaning the house, and doing the laundry for the members of the family. Today, with both adults of the family holding down a job, we have the responsibilities of three careers being placed on the shoulders of two people. Not only must we maintain the career of our choice, but we must maintain the household chores that previous generations assigned to one of the adults exclusively! This will naturally cause feelings of stress, because we feel overwhelmed with all that must get done. (For the men reading this, these home chores are not for the women to do alone! We must share in these, not thinking of it as helping her out with her duties.)

Another growing segment of our population today is composed of single parents. Like dual-income families, these individuals have the responsibilities of two careers being placed on their shoulders! They must maintain a career or job as well as take care of all the tasks of their home. Again, feelings of stress are caused by the overwhelming commitments.

There is an additional obligation that is being placed on both those in dual-income families, as well as single parents, and that is having to take care of elderly parents. Today, people are living longer. Life expectancy has increased dramatically in the past hundred years, and many today are living into their eighties and nineties. As people expect to live longer, it means that much of the responsibility for care is falling on the children of these elderly parents. A *Time* magazine article in February 1999 mentioned that children of elderly parents are providing ten times more health care than the nursing home industry.

Besides the changes in our family units, there are also pressures today because of our consumer-based society. We are inundated with commercials and advertisements wanting us to purchase everything from deodorant to help us smell better, beer in order for us to have three beautiful women hanging all over us, cars that will show our neighbors that we have achieved success, and even financial services that promise to give us the freedom to do what we want when we retire from the grind of everyday business. An underlying message offered by the commercials is that our lives are inadequate because we don't have the product shown on the screen or in our favorite magazine! The message is that everyone is prosperous except us, and if we will only purchase the product, we, too, will have it all and feel content.

The problem is that products and possessions will never make us content. Have you ever experienced a feeling of contentment in your life, only to have this shattered when the neighbors come home with a new car or you see something in the catalog that you would like to have? Your life was perfectly fine before, but now you can't feel that contentment until you possess the object of your desire. So you purchase the object (maybe even get yourself into consumer debt in order to purchase it) and you feel content again. How long does that feeling last? Usually not very long, right?

With the changes in our society, people do often feel overwhelmed and inadequate. These feelings often lead to feelings of stress. But stress is not just an uncomfortable feeling. There are physiological changes that take place in our bodies because of stress.

Our bodies are built for physical stress. By this I mean that our bodies are built for responding to physical dangers of an animal chasing us or someone wanting to harm us in order to take our food or possessions. When we experience a physical danger, our bodies react by making changes internally preparing us for fight or flight! Some of the changes that occur are an increase in our respiration, heart rate, blood pressure, metabolism, and blood flow to the muscles. Though these are appropriate responses when presented with physical stress or danger, they are not appropriate responses for emotional stress, though I was thinking about this last night while watching the Dallas Stars' hockey team.

Maybe fight should be a response to work-related stress. Wouldn't it be great if we could respond like Guy Carboneau of the Stars when an office worker gave us a difficult time? We could whip the fool out of each other until we got tired, and they could exact the same punishment as in hockey for fighting. We would be sent to our offices for two minutes. If we were really bad, we could be sent home for the day and suspended from work for three days. Boy, what kind of deterrent would that be to keeping fighting down?

We would see a rash of these on Friday mornings and Mondays. Give me too much trouble and I'm looking at a three-day weekend!

When our bodies are exposed to the fight or flight response too often without an outlet for these physical changes, our immune system begins to be suppressed. When our immune system is suppressed, we will begin to experience physical illness and injury. Headaches, insomnia, ulcers, high blood pressure, heart disease, even some forms of cancer are being directly tied to stress-related suppression of one's immune system. It is estimated that $150 billion per year is lost by businesses for job-related stress illnesses. Further, it is estimated that 75 percent to 90 percent of physician office visits are related to the stress people feel in their daily lives.

With this in mind, let us begin by first understanding how stressful feelings are manifested within us. Once you understand how these feelings are derived, we will turn our attention to techniques for eliminating them. With the change in perspective which comes from eliminating the stressful feeling, we can ultimately tap into our creative problem solving skills to solve situations that we find stressful.

This book is not going to be one of easy solutions! Too often people want the quick fix to their stress. I, too, wanted this years ago, but I have found that it takes hard work, commitment, and lots of failures to begin to see positive changes in your life. That is the bad news. The good news is that it is worth it! When you change your life, whether it is in response to stress, a relationship, or your physical wellness, it is vastly rewarding! My father-in-law read a book that said we were put on this earth to learn the lessons we needed to learn. Once these had been learned, then we could leave for our rest! No matter what your beliefs about why we are here, you must agree that all of us have room for growth! Whether our afterlife is dependent on our ability to learn these lessons or to grow will remain to be seen, but this growth is vastly rewarding because it is so difficult. Let us begin to ***Let It Go, Just Let It Go!***

CHAPTER 2

Where Do Feelings of Stress Come From?

For there is nothing either good or bad. Thinking makes it so.

—Shakespeare: *Hamlet*

My Grandmother Rowan lived in a house without running water. For those who never had the pleasure of experiencing this, the worst part was not the fact that you had to go outside to the bathroom, even though the cold Missouri winters did make this a bit of an inconvenience. The worst part of living in a house without running water was that water had to be hauled into the house to cook, drink, bathe and clean.

My grandmother's house had a well on its east side in the side yard. This well had an above-ground encasement made out of cement blocks. The top of it had a trapdoor, and above the trapdoor was a pulley. This pulley had a chain through it, and on both ends of the chain buckets were attached. How you got water from the well was you pulled down on the side of the chain with the empty bucket until it was submerged in the well water. This would raise the bucket that had been submerged in the water. You would then pour the contents of the chained bucket into another bucket and carry that bucket into the house for your intended use.

My grandparents wouldn't let us play around the well for fear we would fall in. (They would also not allow us to play on the propane tank because they said these had been known to blow up! As my good friend Michael Johnson would say, "We never knew anyone who had blown up from a propane tank explosion, but we knew there were thousands of people who had died in this tragic and grotesque way because our grandmothers told us so!") About the age of ten, Grandmother Rowan thought we were responsible enough to help get water from the well, and she would send us for it.

My brother Michael was the oldest of all the grandchildren who lived near my grandmother. When he reached the age of ten, she said to Michael, "Say, boy, why don't you go outside to get the water from the well!" It was a big day for Michael and gave the remaining cousins a "right of passage" to look forward to in the future.

Michael, with pride and a bit of a superior attitude, gathered up his jacket and a bucket for his inaugural trip to the well. He was gone about two minutes when we heard him return in a rather accelerated fashion. When he entered the kitchen, he was huffing and puffing, out of breath, white as a sheet, without the water he had been sent to gather!

My grandmother noticed his condition and asked, "Boy, where is the water?" I waited for his reply, less concerned about the water than I was about Michael screwing up the opportunity for the remainder of the grandchildren. I could just see my grandparents talking over the debacle of Michael getting the water and determining that children were not responsible enough to get water alone until they reached the age of forty or fifty.

Michael looked at Grandmother Rowan and said, "I did just as I had seen people do my entire life. I lifted the trapdoor of the well, lowered the empty bucket into the water of the well, and as I reached to pour the water from the other bucket, I noticed a ten-foot long poisonous snake was wrapped around the handle of the bucket. Seeing the snake, I turned tail and ran into the house as quickly as I could!"

My grandmother looked at him with a bit of doubt and explained to him that there were no ten-foot long poisonous snakes in western Missouri, especially at that time of year! At this point, I knew I would never be allowed to get water from the well because I had the unfortunate luck to be the younger brother of a complete moron!

In order to prove to Michael he was wrong, my grandmother took him back to the site of the supposed "snake around the bucket handle," as it became known to future generations of cousins! As my grandmother brought up the bucket, I saw a ten-foot long poisonous snake wrapped around the handle! (My grandmother told us in later years it was a snake about eight to nine inches long, but it sure looked ten-foot long to a five-year-old boy!) When I saw that snake, for the first time in my life I was in agreement with my brother! He had obviously done the right thing by running in the house, and surely my grandmother would see the wisdom in his actions. Maybe my rite of passage of getting water from the well alone wasn't in danger after all.

Much to our chagrin, my tough grandmother grabbed that snake with her bare hand, walked to the middle of the yard and let the snake go in the grass. As the snake slithered under the house, I not only realized I could never set foot in her house again, but said a prayer of thanks to God for allowing my Grandmother Rowan to survive such a foolhardy display of courage!

My old grandmother began to laugh at our fear and told us that the snake was not poisonous but simply a yard snake. She explained all of the positive activities the yard snake provided to the farmer and how it would have been wrong to hurt or kill it! We were hearing nothing of this rationale. How could someone her age not know the imminent danger she had just foolishly put herself in, and why was she rationalizing this activity?

When my grandmother saw her comments were not relieving our fears, she decided to take a different approach. She turned to my brother Michael and said, "Michael, when that snake saw you, it was probably as scared of you as you were of it!"

Michael looked at her and simply said, "Grandma, if that snake was as scared of me as I was of it, that water ain't fit to drink!"

WHAT MAKES YOU FEEL STRESSED?

Many believe the stress in their life comes from a job, children, a spouse, even shows on television! *Time* magazine had a survey that found that a higher percentage of viewers watching Martha Stewart on television felt stress than those watching the evening news! This is a sad statistic. As we get started, write down two or three situations in recent times that you have found stressful. We will return to this later in the chapter.

1.____

____

2.____

____

3.____

____

In a survey that was done on the top ten things people fear, the top item was having to speak in public! Having to speak in public was feared more by the participants of the survey than death, disease, bankruptcy, or even chickens (my biggest fear!). I worked with a man at an accounting firm who was so fearful of speaking in public that one time, as we were walking into a board room to present an audit report, he turned to me and asked if I could do it alone. When my response was in the affirmative, you could see a sense of relief flash over his face. The part of this situation I found baffling was this same person was also a musician, and he did not fear playing in public. He was just petrified to speak in front of a crowd.

Now, there are few things in this life that make my spirit rise more than the thought of getting in front of an audience to speak! Jim Fay of the Love and Logic Institute in Colorado says at the opening of some of his programs that he is glad to be there that day because he found an audience to be his drug of choice! Boy, that is my sentiment over and over again! On the morning of a program, my body wakes up at 4:00–4:30 A.M. ready to go! My excitement is difficult to contain, and it is hard to get through the day if my program is scheduled for the afternoon or even the evening.

How is it that an activity which is the drug of choice for Mr. Fay or myself causes such stress and fear among so many? The explanation of how stress is manifested within us will explain it greatly.

Most of us believe our stressful feelings are inherent to situations. Speaking in front of an audience is just inherently stressful! Having teenage children is naturally stressful. Working at this office or for this boss is inherently stressful. When people believe that the stress they are experiencing is caused by something outside themselves, they will try to change their circumstances in order to change these feelings. Too often they will find that their new circumstances are also stressful.

People are capable of controlling their stress levels, not by changing the situation around them, but by changing their reaction to the situation. In this book, we will discuss how to reduce stress through awareness of the relationship between our thoughts, our feelings, and our moods.

Thoughts

In order to begin the process of reducing our stressful feelings, we must first understand from where these feelings are coming. Our minds are constantly at work, both during our waking hours and our sleeping hours. As we go through our lives, our minds are constantly developing thoughts about things. If you doubt this, try this quick meditation exercise.

Get into a comfortable position, either sitting in a chair or lying on a bed or the floor. As you get comfortable, try focusing your attention on your breathing. As you inhale, notice your stomach expanding and as you exhale, notice your stomach contracting. When inhaling, count to one; and when exhaling, count to two. Continue counting until you reach ten on your fifth exhale and begin the process over again at one. Set a timer for three to five minutes and see how long you can focus your attention on just your breathing.

How long did you go? The full three to five minutes? Were you able to go two minutes? How about a minute? Thirty seconds? Don't feel bad no matter how long you were able to go. This is the nature of meditation, not to control your thoughts, but to witness, in a nonjudgmental way, how your mind will distract you from the prescribed awareness of your breathing! When you notice that your mind is distracted by a thought, you are to observe what caused you to be distracted, then gently bring your mind back to your breathing. If you are able to maintain your mindfulness on your breathing for just a minute the first time out, you have done a great job!

Because of the nature of our mind being constantly at work, let's now explore how feelings are derived. As these words are being written, I find myself feeling very happy! The past ten days have been a vacation for me, and not only have I been home for eighteen straight days, my next trip is nearly two weeks away! It is New Year's Day, and my soul is filled with the optimism usually reserved only for opening day of the baseball season. This coming year promises great things both professionally and personally, so my joy is great today!

William James, the father of American psychology, said, "Thinking is the grand originator of our experiences!" Richard Carlson, in his book *You Can Be Happy No Matter What,* points out that all feelings are first precipitated by a thought. If you feel happy today, as I do, your happy feelings have first been preceded by a happy thought. If you are feeling sad today, your feelings have been preceded by a sad thought. If you are feeling depressed today, your feelings were preceded by a depressing thought. Finally, if you are feeling stressed today, your stressful feelings were preceded by a stressful thought.

When we experience any feeling, no matter what it may be, we have had a thought preceding it. Much of the time it is difficult to recognize this because the feeling happens instantly after our thought, but these are two separate functions. As we experience a situation, our mind instantly has thoughts about it. These thoughts are our attempt to interpret the situation. Based upon this interpretation, we will have an emotional response or feeling. So the thought about the situation is what causes our stressful feeling; the feelings are not inherent to the situation itself.

Michael saw a snake when he drew the bucket from the well. He instantly had thoughts about it being a ten-foot long poisonous snake. These thoughts were his attempt to interpret that situation. Based upon the fearful thoughts he experienced, he had an appropriate emotional response of being scared and running into the house.

My grandmother saw the same snake but had different thoughts about it. She saw a yard snake and thought of the benefits this snake provided to the farmer. These thoughts were her attempt to interpret that situation. Based upon Grandma Rowan's different thoughts, she had the different emotional response of not being scared and allowing the snake the freedom to continue working in conjunction with them to farm the land.

This is one of the best tools you will become armed with to combat the stresses within your life. As you begin to realize the stress you are experiencing is coming from within yourself, you will begin to feel a great deal of power over these circumstances. You no longer have to believe situations are naturally stressful, but you can begin to take control over these feelings because you are the architect of your thoughts.

As you begin to understand this process, you can begin to see circumstances as being neutral in nature. This explains why public speaking can be so stressful for some and invigorating for others. When some are presented with the situation of having to speak in public, they have thoughts which they find stressful. "What if I fail in front of all of those people?" "What will they think of me as a person?" "I will look foolish and even be considered ignorant or stupid." If these thoughts run through a person's mind, how could they not feel stressed when having to speak in public? No one wants to look stupid or foolish in front of others, and the thought of it is stressful.

When I am presented with the opportunity to speak, my thoughts turn to the opportunity to share my message with a group. I remember the times when my message has positively affected members of the audience, and the joy experienced by me and the audience when they hear a story that makes them laugh. I love hearing people laugh, and making others laugh at the stories I share in my programs. These thoughts lead to feelings of joy and positive anticipation, not dread or stress.

Understanding that stressful feelings are derived from your thoughts generated within your own mind and not inherent to situations, you may begin to take control over feelings of stress. Through your awareness as you begin to detect stress within your body—tight muscles, persistent thoughts of doom or fear, or that churning in your stomach—

you can begin to determine what thoughts are causing these feelings.

Before proceeding further, let us look at two aspects of our thoughts.

▶ *When people believe their stressful feelings are inherent to situations they give up control over these feelings.* Because we are the architects of our thoughts, we don't have to allow our thoughts to determine the quality of our lives. We have the option to act or not act upon these.

Our bodies are built with the capability to experience physical pain. When we experience pain, it is a warning sign that there is something causing us physical harm. If you put your hand on a hot pan on the stove, the physical pain of burning tells your mind that there is a physical problem. If you don't move your hand, you will suffer major physical damage to your skin. That message to your brain sends a signal to your hand to move, thus avoiding further damage.

Feelings work the same way as the sensation of pain. The difference is feelings are not warning your mind of physical problems, but emotional problems. When you have any uncomfortable emotion, it is an early warning sign that you are allowing your thoughts to move away from contentment, which is available to us regardless of whatever problems or circumstances we may be experiencing.

When a feeling arises, you have the option of letting these thoughts take control of your life, continuing on to the next thought, which will continue on to another and another until you have what Richard Carlson labeled a "thought attack." Or you can dismiss it as just what it is, a thought. We don't have to take any thoughts seriously. They can be recognized, noted and dismissed without them affecting our current or long-term feelings. Most stress programs offered today try to increase your tolerance to stress. This type of process actually will try to decrease your tolerance to stress by getting you to recognize stress earlier and eliminate the cause of the stress, the thought. It is much like what happened fifty years ago during the study and care of people who had leprosy.

In 1947, Dr. Paul Brand and his wife went to India to study leprosy. Patients with leprosy mysteriously would lose fingers or toes overnight. There wasn't any apparent reason for these infirmities. It was thought that the tissue of the skin was negatively affected by the disease. Dr. Brand did studies of leprosy patients and found their skin tissue was the same as a healthy patient. The mystery continued. One day Dr. Brand discovered, quite by accident, why leprosy patients were losing their limbs. Dr. Brand was trying to open a lock but couldn't turn the key. One of his patients noticed the difficulty and came to help. The patient was able to turn the key but cut his thumb and his forefinger to the bone in doing so! Dr. Brand discovered leprosy diminished a person's sensitivity to pain. His patients didn't experience pain as the rest of us did and thus would hurt themselves because of this!

What Dr. Brand and his wife did with leprosy patients was to help them recognize their pain earlier, thus increasing their awareness to pain. This is what we need to do when it comes to stress. The earlier we recognize that our feelings are coming from our thoughts, the earlier we can begin to let these thoughts go and diminish our stress. With the diminished emphasis being placed on them, we can begin also to let go of the negative emotions.

In his book, Richard Carlson also said, "Ultimately, the relationship you have to your own thinking will determine your mental health and happiness. Do you believe that because you think about something, it must be taken seriously? Or do you understand that thinking is something that you do by virtue of being human, and that you need not confuse thinking with reality? Can you have thoughts and let them pass, in soft focus, or do you feel compelled to contemplate and analyze them?"

This has been the single most important idea I learned when taking control of stress within my life. When presented with stressful feelings, my attention now turns to the thoughts I am experiencing and the awareness that these are composed within my own mind. Then I make the decision to note them and dismiss them as just thoughts.

This may be one of the most difficult disciplines for you to develop. It is easy to see how others' emotions are affected by their thoughts, but not always easy for us to understand the same happens within our own head. Take my word for it, it can be a very powerful and effective tool in the reduction of stress.

▶ *Thoughts are not reality, only our perception of reality.* As we are presented with a situation, we instantly have thoughts about that situation. Our thoughts are our attempt to interpret that situation. Based upon that interpretation, we will have an emotional response. One thing that must be remembered is that these thoughts are just that—our thoughts. They do not necessarily represent reality; they are simply our thoughts about the situation.

When Michael saw the snake on the handle of the bucket, he thought it was a ten-foot long poisonous snake. Obviously his thoughts were not based in reality. They were simply his attempt to interpret the situation he found himself in. Though his thoughts were not based in reality, it didn't make Michael's fear any less.

As you experience situations, your interpretations are not always based in reality. Oftentimes when we take time to see what the reality of the situation is, our perspective changes, thus changing our thoughts and feelings.

The goal is not to control our thoughts. When we try to control our thinking, we will use up immense energy. As Richard Carlson points out, many people believe in "positive thinking." This is the process of telling yourself positive thoughts to replace negative ones, or trying to control your thinking. He points out that thinking a positive thought will make you feel better than thinking a negative one, but it puts tremendous pressure on the individual to maintain these. (My own experiments with positive thinking were frustrating because of the reoccurrence of negative thoughts, especially if these were something which were a fear of mine. Once, when my fitness level was questionable for a big race in Kansas City, I thought my positive thoughts would overcome this, but the persistent negative thought of my impending poor performance continued to arise, no matter how much effort I put into banishing it.)

When we understand that our reality is shaped from the inside out, we begin to take control over stress! As we recognize the thinking process and the fact that positive thoughts need have no more effect on you than negative ones, you will begin to find you don't have to generate thoughts to feel better. All that is required is to recognize that our feelings are coming from our thoughts. This is the first step in learning to let go of our stress!

Stress is not inherent to situations but is the emotional response to your thoughts about these situations. When people begin to take responsibility for their own feelings, they begin to feel the power associated with knowing that since they created these feelings, they can also create more pleasant feelings by changing their perspective on events within their lives and by not taking the negative thoughts so seriously. With this we begin the process of ***Let It Go, Just Let It Go!***

Following this discussion, consider the situations you wrote down at the beginning of this chapter. What were some of the thoughts you had about these situations that caused you stress? Take some time and write about one or two of these on the lines that follow. As you begin to recognize your thought process, you will find your stressful feelings are derived from many of the same thoughts.

1.____

____

____

____

____

____

____

____

____

2.____

____

____

____

____

____

____

____

____

3. ____

____

____

____

____

____

____

____

CHAPTER 3

Moods

Long as the day may be, the night comes at last.

—Old Irish Saying

During my first year of speaking I worked with a national public seminar group while I built up my own speaking business. I was doing any and all programs I could in order to not only earn a living but to get as much experience as possible in a short amount of time. Late that year I was asked to go to Green Bay, Wisconsin, to speak to a group of human resource people regarding critical negotiation skills. I found myself in a bad mood regarding this because I thought, of all the programs I did, this was the worst and I hated delivering it! Not only that, it was November and I was heading from southern Oklahoma to GREEN BAY, WISCONSIN! As a child I remember watching Packers' games on television where the temperature was well below zero, snow flying everywhere, the stadium filled with people whose breath you could see! I didn't really want to go to Green Bay during November. In spite of all these negatives, I really needed the money when they had called me, so I was heading to Green Bay.

I flew from Oklahoma City to Chicago, and when I arrived at the gate at O'Hare for my connecting flight to Green Bay, the ticket agent told me my flight to Green Bay had been canceled. The agent said it would only be a short four-hour wait until the next flight would be departing! I settled into the uncomfortable seat in concourse E of O'Hare airport to read my book and wait out the four hours as pleasantly as possible. My mood was quickly deteriorating, but I thought I would make the best of the situation.

The time arrived for my flight to leave Chicago for Green Bay, and as I handed my boarding pass to the attendant, I discovered that the flight to Green Bay would not be on a jet, but one of those prop planes! You know the kind I am talking about, one of those Buddy Holly-killing planes! I felt my mood move deeper into the recesses toward full-scale depression!

I boarded the flight and found my assigned aisle seat. Sitting with me on my side of the row was a woman in her late forties who was obviously upset. My heart further sunk when I thought of the prospect of the next hour being spent discussing the problems this woman found important enough to show the outward signs of crying, sniffling, and red eyes in front of fifty-two total strangers. I sat down and said, "Hello!" She responded through her sniffles, "Hello." I thought I had fulfilled my obligation as a good traveler; now I could rejoin my book that had become such a good companion during the past four hours in the terminal.

As they started up the motors, my seatmate complimented me on my new dangling cross earring I had purchased during my layover, and then asked, "So where are you from?" I quite innocently said Oklahoma and was greeted with an unusual response. She burst into tears, crying loud enough that the whole plane could hear her, even over the noise of the propellers. I began to realize the entire multitude in the plane was now looking at me, wondering what I had said to this poor woman. I was perplexed by the response since I was the one who had to live there, not her! The next hour offered an answer to her despondent response.

She proceeded to tell me how she had met a man on the Internet and had taken him up on his offer for her to fly from her home near Green Bay to Oklahoma City for a week's visit. She said she arrived on Saturday and found him to be less than honest with her about his life and now, on Tuesday, she was cutting her visit short to return to Green Bay. She said to add insult to injury, she had to call her ex-husband to pick her up at the airport and drive her home because her son had borrowed her car during the week she had planned to be gone. Throughout this conversation, she would rhetorically ask me, "Why can't people tell the truth over the Internet?"

As I arrived at my hotel, feeling weary from the travel, the conversation, and the impending program, my mood was at its lowest. I called my wife, Twyla, immediately on the phone and told her I thought I needed to find a different career because I didn't think this one was working out.

Luckily, not only did I not make that decision while in that night's mood, I found the following day things were different! When I awoke, I realized my hotel was also a casino and sat on grounds surrounded by beautiful fifty-foot trees with a loop around the grounds covering nearly two miles. I was slated to do some long speed work that morning for my training and found the grounds to be ideal for this pursuit.

Following a wonderful workout, I headed to my group and found them to be not only a good group, but one that had a good sense of humor! As I stood in front of a sea of green sweaters, T-shirts and coats, all emblazoned with the famous "G" from the side of the Packers' helmets, I said, "Good morning, my name is Kent Rader, and I am from Oklahoma. You all have some sort of sports team here?" This was greeted with laughter and my day continued to be fantastic.

The day was further enhanced as I finished up the course about 3:45 P.M. and was able to spend about forty-five minutes at the Green Bay Packers' Hall of Fame, across the street from Lambeau Field, the site of all those great Packers games I watched as a child on television. Inside were mementoes of my childhood heroes: Nitschke's helmet that had been pierced as it lay on the ground by a rod of the practice field camera tower that collapsed one day during practice, the yellow practice sweatshirt worn by Coach Lombardi, the locker and duffel bag used by Bart Starr. All the things that had come to life for me as a child when I read the book *Instant Replay* by Jerry Kramer were there in the

Packers' Hall of Fame. I even was able to purchase a Packers T-shirt and sweatshirt as reminders of a wonderful afternoon on the road!

As I boarded my flight for Oklahoma, I began to immerse myself in the wonderful audience attending this program, the history of a team I enjoyed as a child, my own memories of these events that were displayed there, and the lovely fall day in a place I never dreamed I would see. I found my mood rising from the poor temperament with which I had arrived the preceding evening. I still look back upon it as a wonderful experience that I am thankful became part of my life, one that would never have happened if I had let my mood dictate my actions on that gray November night when I was traveling there.

Moods jade your thoughts and thus jade your feelings.

The second component of healthy psychological functioning is that we must understand that our moods are constantly changing and our moods jade our thoughts. When your moods bias your thoughts, they, in turn, bias your feelings. Being able to recognize and differentiate between our abilities between extremes in moods is a major component to understanding our stress as well.

When we are in a good mood, everything looks less formidable, life looks good, and we have a good perspective on situations. We also have access to our creativity when our mood is high. Life and life's circumstances look easier or less intimidating. I often think of this when I am preparing to speak! I love the activity of speaking and find myself waking in a good mood on the day of a performance. I can't wait to go to work and be in front of the audience! On these mornings, I still have the same problems as I have on days like today. There is still death in the world, violence, greed, and money problems. My children are still teenagers and, though they don't experience the quantity of problems of most teenagers, they still have their share. I wake with no fewer responsibilities, nor have the problems associated with an aging body mysteriously disappeared overnight! The only difference is I am in a good mood because I get to go to work on a job I love!

Contrast that with the experience of being in a low or bad mood. When our mood deteriorates, life begins to look unbearable. We take situations more seriously and often misinterpret what people say to us. One of the worst components of a foul mood is that our perspective evaporates, and we lose access to our creative problem solving skills. Our problems are amplified in our mind. The major problem with a bad mood is we want to solve our problems at that moment because that is when they look their worst. If we have a problem that is serious enough to solve when we are in a bad mood, it will still be a problem when we are in a better mood. The difference is we are more inclined to develop an appropriate solution to the problem when we are in a good mood.

This, among the many lessons I have been asked to learn during this lifetime, may be the most difficult for me! I am the classic person who wants to solve his problems when he is in a bad mood because of the immediacy in which they are disguised, like that night in the hotel in Green Bay. I have to consciously force myself to not address problems when I am down because it usually compounds the difficulty instead of resulting in the intended improvement.

Once you begin to understand that your moods, both positive and negative, jade your thoughts and, thus, your feelings, you may begin to recognize certain circumstances where your mood is just naturally higher or lower. As you begin to recognize these situations that naturally alter your mood, you may begin to learn how to circumvent them.

I am in a rather down mood as I write this because I heard the news this morning that Governor Mel Carnahan of Missouri was killed in a plane crash last night, while campaigning for the United States Senate seat. The loss of any life seems to put me in a down mood, but especially the sudden, unexpected loss of life as in Governor Carnahan's case. Though I care little about politics, I know that both Governor Carnahan and Senator Ashcroft, Governor Carnahan's opponent in this race, would make fine senators for not only my home state of Missouri but the country as well, and it is a shame to lose such a grand man and leader.

Another reason such a disaster threw me into a down mood was it brought back memories of an August night in 1976 when Jerry Litton, a congressman from Missouri who was working to get the nomination for the same Senate seat as Governor Carnahan, died in a plane crash following his win in the primary. Not only did Congressman Litton lose his life, but his wife and children, along with a friend and his son, lost their lives in the calamity. I remember meeting Jerry Litton and being impressed with his abilities. I cried that night at the loss for our state, but more importantly, for my feelings of loss.

I have in my office a plaque that states, "Happy are those who dream dreams and are willing to pay the price to see them come true." This was a quote from Congressman Litton, and it meant a great deal to me. I kept that beside my bed for a long time, so it was the first thing I saw when I awoke for my early morning runs in the fall and winter during my senior year at Richmond High School. It helped me through the death of my Grandmother Rader that winter and on many other mornings when I would rather have returned to my nice warm, comfortable bed instead of lacing up those old running shoes and heading out for my runs!

Though the loss of Jerry Litton turned out all right from a political scenario (John Danforth won the seat and distinguished himself, in my opinion, as one of the most prominent senators of our time), I still am reminded of the sadness of that night when a similar situation happens. It seems to always put my mood into a downward spiral.

Knowing my mood is low today helps me be wary that things may look more formidable than they really are. This chapter hasn't gone well and the dejected mood I find myself in will accentuate that feeling. Just writing these words has helped me understand this situation better.

I have been traveling consistently for the past six years, and when my own awareness with regard to moods began to expand, I noticed that the day or two before leaving on a trip my mood would begin to deteriorate. It usually began when I started to pack for my trips. I understand that travel is an indispensable part of my career as a speaker, but it still throws me into a dejected humor. I can really relate to the Steve Miller song *Jet Airliner*. I often play this song on my way to the airport to remind me that travel is an unavoidable part of this career.

Once I took notice that my mood was consistently degenerating just before my trips, I could begin to take steps to help with this. One of the most important adjustments I have made is immediately upon returning home from a trip I do my laundry and pack my bags for the next trip. I am always in a great mood when I return home, so the packing of my belongings doesn't bring me down. This way I am packed when the time comes for me to load up my car for the next trip to the Will Rogers World Airport in Oklahoma City and wherever my journey may take me.

It is important to remember that our moods are constantly changing, and they affect our thoughts. There are different capacities available to us as our mood changes from bad to good. If there are problems that are serious enough to try to solve when we are in a bad mood, they will still be problems when we are in a good mood, but at least we will have a better perspective on them and will have access to our creativity in order to solve them! As you find yourself in a bad mood, don't allow it to take over, but ride it out and you will find you are now beginning to ***Let It Go, Just Let It Go!***

Let It Go—Just Let It Go!

CHAPTER 4

Writing

Writing is like breathing, it's possible to learn to do it well, but the point is to do it no matter what.

—Julia Cameron, *The Right to Write*

I want to personally thank Mrs. Spurgen and Mrs. Swafford, my kindergarten and first grade teachers, respectively, for helping me learn two of the most positive tools I have ever known in helping me lead a more enjoyable life. They helped me learn how to read and write, two activities that have served me well. I find few activities more enjoyable than reading. I love nothing better than to spend my weekend afternoons listening to the St. Louis Cardinals baseball games on the television, as I listened to them on the radio when I was a kid, drinking a cold Dr Pepper and reading a book. I can't tell you how many wonderful hours and books I have consumed in this fashion.

I love biographies, and two of my favorites are *Truman* by David McCullough and *Clarence Darrow for the*

Defense by Irving Stone. The former was written at my alma mater, William Jewell College, while Mr. McCullough was a writer in residence there. Eastern philosophy books, such as *Awakening the Buddha Within* by Lama Surya Das and *The Art of Happiness* by the Dalai Lama, have become a mainstay in my stable of books during the past twelve years as I have wanted to improve my personhood. I also love humorous books like Drew Carey's *Dirty Jokes and Beer,* or *Ball Four* by Jim Bouton.

I love the job I have today, being a professional speaker and author, but should I ever retire, I envision retirement being spent reading my beloved books for one last time before leaving this earth. Coke Stevenson, the governor of Texas who was defeated by Lyndon Johnson in the 1948 Senate election, did much the same following his retirement from the arena of politics. This love of reading has given me pleasure that I could never recount in the limited scope of writing this book.

Besides reading, I find writing to be an enjoyable activity, but it is the therapeutic side of writing that has led me to the subject of this chapter. Now that we are aware that our feelings of stress are derived from our own thoughts about situations, we can begin to change our perspective about these situations so we can eventually access our creative problem solving skills. One of the finest ways to changing this perspective is by using writing!

It has been discovered that writing about life's stressful events actually improves our physical health. Let me tell you about some researchers who tested this. They took a group of patients who suffered from asthma and rheumatoid arthritis and divided them into two groups. They asked the first group of patients to write for twenty minutes for three consecutive days about life's most stressful events—the death of loved ones, major illnesses, loss of job or money. Whatever they found stressful within the context of their lives they should write about for three consecutive days, twenty minutes per day.

The other group of patients were also asked to write for three consecutive days, twenty minutes per day, but instead of writing about stressful events, they were asked to write about their plans for the future.

The study found that the people who wrote about their life's stressful events had significant reductions in their symptoms of asthma and rheumatoid arthritis, while the group writing about their plans for the future had no significant reductions in their symptoms. *The Journal of the American Medical Association,* which reported on this study, is quoted as saying,"This is the first study to demonstrate that writing about stressful life experiences improves physician ratings of disease and objective indices of disease." Writing about your stressful events in your life can actually improve your physical health!

A fine example of this is a book by Judy Jacklin Belushi entitled *Samurai Widow.* Ms. Belushi wrote almost daily about her thoughts, feelings, fears and recovery following the loss of her husband, John Belushi, to a drug overdose in 1982. What a wonderful representation of the healing powers of writing when it comes to events in our lives that we not only find stressful but devastating! During my reading of this book, my thoughts would turn to situations in my own life that generated a parallel feeling. Seeing someone recover from such a traumatic experience offered me hope of my own recovery from life's ordeals.

This chapter will offer you two ways you may implement writing into your life in order to better handle stress.

The first comes from a book titled *The Artists' Way* by Julia Cameron. Julia Cameron wrote *The Artists' Way* to help people recover their creativity, and she offers a mechanism known as "morning pages" to assist in this recovery. I have found it to be a wonderful tool in helping reduce feelings of stress in my life.

"Morning pages" consist of three longhand written pages of stream-of-consciousness writing first thing each morning. Julia Cameron calls these "Brain Drain." There are no right or wrong ways to do these pages. Basically, whatever comes to your mind, put it down on the page until you fill up three pages of longhand writing on a daily basis. Something about physically writing these pages helps one get in touch with one's essence, one's purpose and one's mental balance.

A few reasons you may want to try morning pages in your daily lives are as follows:

- When morning pages are done on a daily basis, you will find they become a form of meditation. Like any meditation practice, you will find it helps you become and remain more centered and balanced as a person. You may also find yourself focusing more on the priorities in your life and not being distracted by situations that in the long run have little, if any, consequence.

▶ When you incorporate morning pages into your daily routine, you will begin to make the connection between how your thoughts are the generator of whatever you are feeling. You will also begin to notice how your mood influences your thoughts. Writing will help you take notice of your thoughts when you are in a dejected mood, thus helping you begin to see for yourself how your mood affects your feelings.

▶ Finally, writing on a daily basis will allow you to begin the process of not taking any of your thoughts too seriously. As you begin to not place too much importance on your thoughts, you will find your stressful thoughts having less and less control over you.

Three years ago I began the discipline of writing morning pages. At that time in my life, I desperately wanted to begin a career of writing and speaking, but, like so many in today's society, feared the loss of the perceived security I felt from having a job with a company. These pages allowed me to overcome this fear and pursue a calling which I love! They have become my form of meditation, allowing me to make the connection between my feelings and my thoughts, put less stock in the moods I experience from day to day, plus help me keep my priorities in the forefront of my daily thoughts.

I spend the first forty-five minutes to an hour of my day writing my thoughts. I absolutely love the activity of rising at 5:00 A.M., sitting on a cushion on the floor of my office, a box of books serving as a desk for my spiral notebook of morning pages, and a steaming cup of coffee in my left hand. There are days these pages are done in hotel rooms while I am traveling, sometimes on airplanes, but no matter where, they have become an important component of my day. At times my pages resemble the rambling of the compulsive individual that Twyla and the children have grown to know and love. There are other days they are filled with insight, not only into my own thinking, but into the problems and stresses I am experiencing at the time. And at other times, they offer me creative solutions to my current problems. When I am unable to do this activity, I find I truly miss it, and I am not as centered on the priorities of the day or my life. These pages have made a major difference in how I handle the stresses I encounter from day to day.

As you begin your practice of morning pages, there are just a couple of things you should keep in mind. These are as follows:

- These pages are meant for your eyes only and are not intended for others to read! If others are privy to these pages, you may find yourself compromising what you are writing and defeat the whole purpose of the pages.

▶ Your thoughts are neither good nor bad, they are simply your thoughts. With regard to thoughts and writings, these are to be done in a nonjudgmental way, just as any meditation practice. Actions, not thoughts, should be classified as good or bad. Don't be too hard on yourself.

▶ You should not read them for the first few months you are writing. If you read your morning pages too soon, you may also begin to censor yourself because you may not believe you are writing correctly. You do not want to compromise your thoughts through being overly critical of your writing, and this may happen before you make these a part of your daily routine. Just come to the page every day and write.

▶ I enjoy the activity of writing first thing in the morning, and Julie Cameron says it is not negotiable, that these must be written first thing in the morning. There are some individuals who do not enjoy rising at 5:00 A.M. I know it is hard to believe, but some people like to sleep later into the day and stay up past 8:00 P.M.! Go figure! Anyway, my wife, Twyla, is one of these sick individuals, and she finds writing first thing in the morning more stressful than helpful! (She finds having to do anything before 11:00 A.M. stressful! This does not bode well for being a public school art teacher! You would think they would be more understanding of individual needs and begin school around 1:00 P.M. for her, wouldn't you?) She experimented with morning pages a couple of years ago and found that writing first thing in the morning was actually detrimental for her. She has found writing in the evening is of benefit for her when she takes the time to do it. I would encourage you to write pages when you find them to be of benefit. They don't have to be done first thing in the morning! JUST WRITE, no matter the time of day!

There are some who don't want to commit the time it takes to write three consecutive pages each day. Though it would be my suggestion to try morning pages for at least thirty days, there is another way to receive the positive benefits of writing when it comes to recognizing and reducing your stress.

I am originally from Richmond, Missouri, and am proud of the fact that no matter where I live, I will always be from Missouri! Richmond sits only forty miles from Independence, Missouri, the home of our thirty-third president, Harry S. Truman. President Truman learned at an early age that when he felt the negative emotions of stress or anger, if he would write as fast and furious as possible about the situation that he was experiencing, he could get all of these emotions out on the page and be able to access a clear, more creative mind. He called these writings "longhand spasm," and they became commonplace during his life.

Like suggested with the practice of morning pages, most of the time President Truman intended these to be for his eyes only. He would simply get these emotions out on the page and then store these in his personal belongings until the crisis passed. Once the crisis had passed, he would destroy these.

Many of President Truman's longhand spasms are included in letters to his beloved wife, Bess. Though she would have access to these innermost personal thoughts, he felt they were safe in the confidence of his soul mate.

One of my favorite President Truman stories took place around Christmas 1955, three years after leaving the office of President of the United States. President Truman walked into the living room of their house at 219 North Delaware in Independence to find Bess pitching his letters into a blazing fire in the fireplace! President Truman asked Bess what she was doing. She responded that she was burning his letters. When he asked her why, she stated she had read them and knew what they said, so she didn't feel the need to continue to keep them. President Truman, indignant that anyone would destroy something a President had written, appealed to Mrs. Truman by asking her to think of history! Mrs. Truman was said to have responded, "Harry, I am!" as she continued to burn the letters of a lifetime!

There are still over 1,200 letters from Mr. Truman to his wife that survived the fire of 1955, and they are housed today in the Truman Library in Independence. President Truman used the venue of his letters to Bess to vent his frustrations, stresses and feelings of fear. He also used longhand spasms to just release pent up frustrations.

President Truman's most famous longhand spasm came at Christmastime in 1950. Come with me, if you will, to this critical period in the life of our thirty-third President. The Korean War is at a crucial juncture and, on December 5, 1950, during meetings with British Prime Minister Attlee, Charlie Ross, the President's press secretary and boyhood friend from Independence, dropped dead of a heart attack while preparing for a news conference for NBC television. President Truman not only had the stress of a war that had the potential of turning into World War III, but now he had lost one of his most trusted advisors and friends.

President Truman tried to read a prepared tribute to Mr. Ross, but broke down during it and said, "Ah, hell, I can't read this thing. You fellows know how I feel anyway . . . ."

That evening, Mrs. Truman and the President attended a concert in Constitution Hall featuring his daughter, Margaret, who was trying to develop a singing career. Though he is said to have looked "downcast" during the performance, he carried through with his family responsibilities while the responsibilities of the most powerful office in the world rested squarely upon his shoulders.

The following morning, President Truman woke at his usual hour of 5:30 A.M. and, in the Blair House where he and Mrs. Truman were living during renovations of the White House residential quarters, he read a scathing criticism of his only child's musical performance in the *Washington Post* by music critic Paul Hume! With the stress and grief President Truman was feeling at the time, he snapped!

Pulling out a piece of White House stationery and a pen, he formulated his most famous longhand spasm. It went as follows:

Mr. Hume:

I've just read your lousy review of Margaret's concert. I've come to the conclusion that you are an "eight ulcer man on four ulcer pay."

It seems to me you are a frustrated old man who wishes he could have been successful. When you write such poppy-cock as was in the back section of the paper you worked for it shows conclusively that you're off the beam and at least four of your ulcers are at work.

Someday I hope to meet you. When that happens you'll need a new nose, a lot of beefsteak for black eyes, and perhaps a supporter below! Westbrook Pelger, a gutter snipe, is a gentleman alongside you. I hope you'll accept that statement as a worse insult than a reflection on your ancestry.

President Truman sealed the envelope, placed his own three-cent stamp, and asked a White House messenger to mail the letter for him. Though the *Washington Post* and Mr. Hume responded appropriately by taking no action, copies of the letter were made and it appeared on page one of the tabloid *Washington News*. Though the sanity of our

President was questioned by newspapers, including the *Chicago Tribune,* Mr Truman stood by the longhand spasm. He agreed that he should not have mailed it, but felt he had the right, even duty, to represent two people. He was both the President of the United States and a father. The letter represented the feelings and actions of being a father.

My own experience with longhand spasms has proven to be very beneficial. I have utilized these during periods which I find stressful, especially when having to deal with situations or people where I believe confrontation is inevitable or warranted. When we are emotionally charged during a confrontation, we sometimes say things which are harmful to a long-term relationship with that person. I have been guilty of this far too many times in my own lifetime. A few years ago, after reading about President Truman's longhand spasms, I began using them to get my emotions out of my system before entering into a conflict with someone else in order to not say something which I will regret later.

I still too often fly off the handle with situations where my emotions overtake my better judgment, but I continue to grow in this regard via the use of longhand spasms. I pull out a sheet of paper when my emotions begin to get the best of me and try to pour all of these onto the page. When my opportunity arises to discuss the situation with the person I am having difficulties with, I find I am more calm because the emotion is on the page, not in my head!

In my travels, I have had others tell me they have found writing similar to longhand spasms to be beneficial during forlorn periods of time such as following the loss of a loved one or the end of a love relationship. One woman at a conference in Houston told me she learned about the use of this type of writing during her teens. She said following the breakup of her first true romance of her life at the age of eighteen, she was depressed and disheartened. She said she struggled with the feelings of loneliness, hurt, and loss for a number of months.

One night, when she was having difficulty sleeping, she pulled out a piece of paper and penned a letter to her ex-lover. She said she got off her chest all the painful, hurtful feelings she was experiencing, and she immediately felt better. She said it didn't matter that she had not intended on mailing this letter, nor that he would never know of this pain she was experiencing, she felt better just getting it out of her system. She was so astonished at the positive effect it had on her. She said that when she would begin to feel herself being dragged back into that state of despondency, she would simply write this man another letter. Eventually the pain diminished and she was able to resume her normal activities.

She told me she has used this same tool during other times in her life when painful emotions have paralyzed her in her daily life. She said she uses it when she lacks the courage to confront someone who has harmed her in some way. She said she writes out all the things she would like to say to this person but doesn't have the fortitude to say. She says the act of writing it has the same positive emotional effect on her as if she spoke it to the person.

No matter how they are utilized, if you get the emotions out on the page, you will find you will eventually come to the point where you have a more clear, creative mind to deal with your problematic situation.

Regardless of your choice of morning pages or long-hand spasms, I would encourage you to keep these for your eyes only. Writing not only makes us feel physically better, but can also help you:

- Take the emotion out of the situation.

- Put situations into the proper perspective.

- Work out solutions to problems with a clearer head.

- Keep centered and on track with your life.

- Keep problems in perspective, regardless of your mood.

- Improve your mood and allow you to *Let It Go, Just Let It Go!*

CHAPTER 5

Humor

If we don't have a sense of humor, we lack a sense of perspective.

—Wayne Thiebaud, *artist*

Like most couples who have a long history, Twyla and I have had our periods of difficulty! During one of the most difficult periods of our marriage, we were talking with a counselor, and she asked us what had kept us together for such a long time. We answered in unison, "It is because we almost always are able to laugh, no matter how bad things get!" Twyla has a wonderful sense of humor, and it may be the facet I love most about her.

Two years ago I was speaking at a conference of nurses. Not only was it one of the largest audiences I had ever presented in front of, it was a new program that had never been performed. To complicate matters, the opening story was about the day my mother-in-law died of cancer. I loved Twyla's mom very much and doubted I could recount the details without crying. I was delivering a new program to the largest group I have ever been in front of and I start with the hardest story I know. I was feeling the pressure that morning while we waited for the opening keynote speaker to finish.

As we were waiting backstage, Twyla could sense my nervousness by my constant pacing. My obsessive comments of the reasons for this nervousness about the program were wearing on her, so I felt a change was in order. I looked at her and asked, "In your wildest dreams, did you ever think I would be talking in front of a group this large?" She looked at me with the straightest face ever and simply said, "In my wildest dreams, you never show up!" I began to laugh and instantly felt a wave of calm come over me. That performance was the best of my career up to that point, thanks to Twyla's ability to make me laugh.

Cancer is probably the most unfunny thing in the world,
but I'm a comedian, and even cancer can't stop me
from seeing humor in what I went through.

—Gilda Radner

Humor enables us to experience joy even when faced with adversity, low mood and stressful times. As you experience stressful feelings in your life, you can count on humor to be one of the quickest ways of changing your perspective on events.

Numerous studies have shown the positive physical and emotional effects of humor. Socrates said, "As it is not proper to cure the eyes without the head, nor the head without the body, so neither is it proper to cure the body without the soul." I have found a sense of humor to be one of the components of my soul and continue to find how humor has offered me the opportunity to help cure both my body and my head.

One of the first to notice the positive physiological effects of humor was Norman Cousins. As he wrote in his book *Anatomy of an Illness,* Norman Cousins was stricken with a serious collagen illness in the 1960s and "had a fast-growing conviction that a hospital was no place for a person who was seriously ill." He decided to take his recovery into his own hands, so he moved out of the hospital and into a hotel in New York City. He understood from a book by Hans Selye titled *The Stress of Life* that there were negative physiological effects on the body due to negative emotions like anger, stress and frustration. He wondered if there would be positive physiological effects on the body due to positive emotions like laughter and love.

When he moved into the hotel, he began to experiment with certain vitamins and laughter. He would watch movies, often of the Marx Brothers and "Candid Camera" reruns. Much to his delight, he found that "ten minutes of genuine belly laughter had an anesthetic effect and would give me at least two hours of pain-free sleep."

Lee Burk, Ph.D., of Loma Linda University School of Medicine found that as we laugh our immune system is stimulated because of changes in our blood system. Dr. Burk found our serum cortisol levels begin to decrease and our active t-lymphocytes begin to increase when we laugh. Both of these stimulate our immune system. Remember from earlier, prolonged exposure to the physiological changes in our body that take place when our system moves into the "fight or flight" response will suppress our immune system. As we laugh, we offset the negative changes that take place in our body from experiencing stress.

Dr. Hans Selye also wrote another book titled *Stress Without Distress*. In this book, he agrees with Richard Carlson by saying that stressful feelings are dependent upon our perception and our thoughts of events. He states that humor gives us a different perspective on events and thus will change our stressful feelings.

One of the studies that I love to quote is by Patty Wooten. Ms. Wooten runs a company named Jest For The Health of It. She experimented with how 231 American nurses would respond if they were not only encouraged to laugh, but taught how to find the humorous side to things during a six-hour humor training course.

Her findings "indicate that if (people are) encouraged and guided to use humor, they can gain a sense of control in their life. We cannot control events in our external world, but we have the ability to control how we view these events and the emotional response we choose to have to them."

How can we learn to laugh, especially during the feelings of stress and pain? Though it is difficult to laugh during a stressful time because the events are serious in nature, it may be the most important time to do so. I am going to outline three practices that you may try to bring more humor into your life.

Associate with People Who See the Humorous Side to Situations

The first approach is to associate with people who have the ability to see humor in the daily situations which present themselves. This has been one of the most important findings of my life! Not only will they help us laugh, they will help us learn how to find the humorous side to situations, and we can begin to learn to develop our own ability to see the humor of day-to-day events.

I once worked in a hospital in Sedalia, Missouri. I remember one of the daily pleasantries was getting to see Neil, the director of respiratory therapy. Neil was a short man who had questionable personal hygiene habits. He smoked one cigarette after another and did this during management meetings! Though Neil had some habits that were less that desirable, he did have the uncanny ability to see the humorous side to situations and events. I remember on numerous stressful occasions he would come out with an unusual observation. Because of this fact, I rather enjoyed having him in the meetings of the hospital, as there were few others involved who were such fun.

On one occasion, following a difficult manager's meeting, Neil broke the group's tension by asking our maintenance man how to pronounce a name of one of his vendors.

If you think accountants are anal retentive, you should meet some of the maintenance men who work in hospitals. This particular manager was so much so, he even had a pocket protector in his shirt every day. This pocket protector was always filled with gauges, pens, and folded pieces of paper. Though many of these papers surely must have been important, all seemed destined for the same fate of being folded into an eighth of their original size and to spend eternity in his pocket protector. On the front of this pocket protector was the name of one of the vendors of the maintenance department.

Following this particular meeting, Neil, with a cigarette dangling from his lips, asked the maintenance director how he pronounced the name of that vendor, as it was spelled "S-E-X-A-U-E-R." The maintenance director proudly and without hesitation said, "It is pronounced SEX HOUR!" Neil looked at him and said to the rest of us, "Man, I rarely get lunch!" The tension felt by everyone in the room was instantly lifted, as we howled with laughter. We returned to our departments to deal with the unpleasant situation of cutting hours, all feeling a bit better because of the laughter.

Enjoy things you find funny

The second technique is for you to take time to enjoy things you find funny. Movies, books, recordings and television offer great opportunities for this. I don't always take the time to do this, but my favorite thing is to return from one of my trips and spend Saturday or Sunday afternoon watching movies that I enjoy and find funny. Some of my favorites include *Men In Black, A League of Their Own, Slap Shot,* and *Blazing Saddles*. One movie that I really enjoy when my life seems overburdened is *As Good As It Gets*.

Twyla and I went to see *As Good As It Gets* at the picture show, and I believe no one laughed louder than us! The reason is that it wasn't Jack Nicholson up there on the screen, it was Kent Rader! I am one of the most compulsive people you will ever meet! I eat Oreo cookies three at a time, one from each row as it makes it easier to wrap the package up in order to keep the remaining cookies fresh! My children have been trained from early in their childhood to eat Oreo cookies in multiples of three so they could keep from contaminating the package! Now that they are teenagers, they will eat them in multiples of three, but they will eat them all out of one row just to send me over the deep end!

I put my socks and shoes on first thing in the morning and only remove them to shower or go to bed. The worst part of this is they must go on in a particular order. First my left sock, then my left shoe, followed by my right sock and my right shoe. I don't really know the reason for this one, but follow it with the rigidity of a religious ritual.

I do wash my hands excessively and feel better eating meals at the same time of the day! One of the finest cures for me taking my life too seriously is to watch *As Good As It Gets*. It seems to naturally put things back into perspective for me, especially stressful situations.

As I mentioned earlier, I love to read, and some of the books I enjoy reading because of humor include *Ball Four* by Jim Bouton and *Dirty Jokes and Beer* by Drew Carey. I cannot repeat any of the jokes from the book by Drew Carey here. If you are the type to be easily offended, please don't pick this book up and, if you do, wash your hands because it is filthy. If Drew doesn't suit your taste, read any of the books by Bill Cosby, especially the one titled *Fatherhood* as it is a classic.

I do have certain television shows I enjoy but find the danger with television is you will watch not only the stuff you enjoy, but will sit through stuff you don't enjoy. Have you ever noticed some of the afternoon talk shows are almost hypnotic? Sometimes I find myself having watched Sally or Jerry for ten minutes and want to ask, "Who let me watch this?" I would not advocate watching TV for the sake of watching. Watch the shows you find enjoyable and turn the rest off! I have found during the times of my life when I am really down, I will sit in front of the TV and want to do nothing but vegetate. This cannot be a healthy response to life's troubles but seems to be one I am inclined to do.

Develop your own ability to see the humorous side

The final strategy I will suggest is to develop your own sense of humor. This may be the biggest order yet, as it is very difficult to see the humorous side of things when we are immersed in the situation causing thoughts and feelings of stress. This may be one of the most important stress reduction skills you can develop.

How do you develop the ability to see the humorous side to things? Well, you must look for the comical components of the situation. I began to see the humorous side to things first by seeing the humorous side to situations in retrospect. As I developed this skill, I was then able to implement it in current situations so I could begin to see the humorous side at the time that situation was happening.

Earlier this year, during a program at the Susan B. Allen Hospital in El Dorado, Kansas, one of the maintenance workers, John, was sitting on the front row. It came to my attention that he was wearing the very same Sexauer pocket protector as the director of maintenance did fifteen years ago. When it came time for me to tell the story about Neil, I had John come to the front of the audience. I went through the anecdote and, when it came time to pronounce the company name, John said, "sex hour," right on cue. I told them Neil's comment about rarely getting lunch and got the usual laughter.

About twenty minutes later, someone's watch alarm began to go off. Now this was an intimate group meeting of managers, so I was not using a microphone for the program. Usually my voice carries fine, but, without a microphone, I find other noises to be a bit distracting. It took me a minute, but I realized that the alarm was coming from John's watch! I knew everyone in the room could hear it and, since he was sitting on the front row, it was difficult to ignore. Instead of letting it bother me as these things sometimes do, I decided to change my perspective on the situation and use humor. Just about the time it ended, I said, "Well, we won't be seeing John for an hour."

Mark Twain said, "The secret source of humor is not joy, but sorrow." I also believe it is often cruelty. In this case, John took the comment very well and the group enjoyed a hearty laugh because of it. Had this been allowed to bother me, we would have missed that opportunity. Thank you, John, for being such a good sport.

Now one of the positive aspects of using humor in your day-to-day situations is you help others develop a sense of humor. Joseph Michelli, Ph.D., the author of *Humor, Play and Laughter, Stress-Proofing Life with Your Kids,* advocates the use of humor with your children in order to help them develop the ability to see the humorous side to things. As children develop the ability to see the humorous side, they will be more inclined to use humor in stressful situations in their lives.

Now the thing I must tell you is that Twyla and I decided we wanted to work with our children differently than our parents had dealt with us, so we decided to use humor with our children from the very beginning. It is true, if you use humor with your children, they will develop a sense of humor, but the problem is they develop your sense of humor. We have noticed this with our son, Keith.

Keith is one of the most refreshing and good-natured people you will ever meet. He has been an absolute joy to be around, even as he has reached his mid-teens. About a year ago, upon reaching the age of fifteen, the state of Oklahoma deemed him mature enough to drive, providing one of his parents would risk their lives in the car with him. He obtained his learner's permit and began driving.

His mother was the one who drove most of the time with him because they go to the same school, and it is a twenty-six-mile drive each way. Besides, I travel so much and . . . I am a chicken! Well, the first time I rode with him, I found this to be stressful.

I made an enormous mistake with my children when they were small. We would be driving in the car and they would be complaining about the music. I would turn to them and say, "Listen, you will listen to the Rolling Stones because I'm the one driving the car!" Well, let me tell you, that is a stupid mistake that will come back to haunt you. I was telling this story in a program in Montana six months ago, and someone in the audience came to me after the program and said she thought, having been trained as an accountant, I would have thought of saying that they would listen to my music because I was the one paying for the car. This would have avoided this situation. Well, I should have, but didn't!

That boy got into the car, buckled his seat belt, turned the radio to one of his stations, and looked at me saying, "You will listen to the Dead Crows (maybe it was the Counting Crows, I don't remember) because I am the one driving the car!" Boy, if I ever felt like hitting him, it was in that moment!

The boy began driving and could tell not only was I tense because I was riding in the seat of death for the first time with him driving, but now I was listening to this crappy music that I didn't enjoy at all. The tension in the car could have been cut with a knife, but I must have been living right on this day because as the Dead Crow's song ended, the news began. We were only a couple of miles from our destination, and I thought surely the news will last until we get there.

The boy continued to drive in the tense atmosphere, and I know he was looking for a way to change the perspective on the events of the moment. The final news story of the day was about the Psychic Friends Hotline! (You remember them, with Dionne Warwick and all.) Well, it seems that the Psychic Friends Hotline was experiencing some difficulty. As I say in my program, that boy of mine ain't quite right! The story said that the Psychic Friends Hotline had declared bankruptcy. The boy looked at me and said, "You would have thought they would have seen that coming." I instantly laughed, and the whole atmosphere of the driving experience changed!

As you use humor in your daily lives, you find it does the following:

- Humor fortifies perspective. It allows us to give stressful thoughts less emphasis.

- Humor improves our moods, making our lives seem less bleak and unbearable.

- Laughter not only releases uncomfortable emotions, it offsets negative physical changes, making us feel better physically and allowing us to ***Let It Go, Just Let It Go!***

Let It Go—Just Let It Go!

Chapter 6

Physical Activity

Attention to health is life's greatest hindrance.

—Plato

Now, before you set this book aside because you don't want to read another runner's promotion of running as the one and only activity you should engage in, let me tell you that the physical activity discussed here is not just organized aerobic and strength workouts.

Last year, following a program in Burns Flat, Oklahoma, a good friend and fellow speaker of mine, Gary Davis, told me he didn't think I should talk too much about physical exercise. He said even though he exercised and agreed with my thoughts about how physical exercise helps with stress and the day-to-day problems of life, he thought people didn't want to hear that message because of their own physical inactivity. I didn't change my program because of disagreement with Gary's thoughts, but my opinion changed that summer when I read a new book by Peg Jordan, R.N., titled *Fitness Instinct.*

In the book, Ms. Jordan does a wonderful job of talking about physical activity, not organized workouts like so many other gurus of fitness. She points out that the latest *United States Surgeon General's Report on Physical Activity and Health* states that only 20 percent of our population exercises consistently for an hour, three to four times per week. In a society that is inundated with fitness magazines and books, there must be something wrong with the message that is being delivered on wellness, including my own.

This chapter will hopefully give you not only the positive benefits of activity for stress reduction but give you some ideas for engaging in this activity. The key is to find activities that you enjoy and will become a part of your daily life. Though mine may be running, yours could be just taking a daily walk or getting a weekly massage. No matter, take time to use your body, as there are many positive stress-related benefits to this activity.

When talking about physical activity, it is important first to know the positive effects physical activity has upon our stressful feelings and the physical changes that take place during feelings of stress. These are as follow:

- When you are physically active, your body releases hormones known as endorphins. The word *"endorphin"* is derived from the word *"morphine"* and implies that a morphine is internally produced within our bodies. It's been found that endorphins are a more powerful painkiller than morphine and, in recent studies, have been found to be more powerful than all but one of the prescription antidepressant drugs available at the current time.

▶ When you are engaged in a physical activity, regardless of what that activity is, your mind will be focused on the activity instead of the persistent thoughts that cause you stress.

▶ When you are physically active, you give your body an outlet for the psychological changes caused by stressful thoughts when your body begins the fight or flight response. You will remember from the beginning of the book, as our bodies experience stress, they can't recognize the difference between physical stress, such as someone attacking us, versus emotional stress, such as your sixteen-year-old son washing his clothes, AGAIN, with a blue ink pen in them! As we are physically active, our bodies have an outlet for the psychological changes caused by the fight or flight response, thus not allowing these changes to build up within us and cause our immune system damage.

▶ Physical activity enhances your self-image. As your self-image is enhanced, it give you a feeling of control over your life, thus helping you with the feelings of stress.

With the positive benefits of physical activity outlined above and before we get into specifics of physical activity with regard to stress reduction, let's discuss focusing our attention on our breathing.

Focusing attention on your breathing is an Eastern meditation method meant to help you become more mindful of the present moment and how your mind is constantly at work to take you away from the moment. You may use this also to receive the stress-reducing benefits of physical activity. Many who exercise on a consistent basis don't always receive the stress-reduction benefits because they aren't present in the activity. Their bodies are engaged in physical activity, but their minds are engaged in activities other than the workout! If your mind continues to obsess on the thoughts that are causing you stress, you won't receive the full benefit of the activity.

One of the easiest ways to be present is to focus on your breathing, the same as meditation practitioners do when they first begin what is described as "sitting" meditation. It is like the breathing meditation practice you tried in the chapter regarding your thoughts. While exercising, your attention should be focused on your breathing, as your breathing is always with you and always available for your attention. (If it isn't, you need to put this book down and get medical attention!) When you focus on your breathing, let it be natural. Don't attempt to change your breathing, just let it be! Watch your stomach expand as you breathe in (this is caused by the pushing down of the diaphragm as your lungs expand) and contract as you exhale. When you focus your attention on your breathing, what you will find is your mind gets distracted. This is natural so don't be discouraged by this circumstance!

As you find your attention is no longer on your breathing, note how your attention got off your breathing and gently move your attention back to your breathing. Don't get upset with your mind or judge these changes in thought as good or bad, just something that happens, like the weather.

Your attention will remain on your breathing for a while, then you will become aware that your attention is now on another thought that has popped into your head. Again, notice how your mind wandered to these thoughts and gently, without judgment, move your attention back to your breathing.

Focusing your attention on your breathing is just one method. You can focus your attention on anything. During my running, my attention is on my breathing, my heart rate via a heart rate monitor, plus physical areas of my body that are currently troublesome, including my sciatic nerve on my left side and my right achilles tendon. This morning, during a longer run, I noticed my attention wandered from these details to thoughts about my schedule for this Saturday, including the workout I was planning for that day. These thoughts of the workout took me in the direction of an article that I noticed in a running magazine about using a heart rate monitor for that type of workout. About this time, my attention was brought to these thoughts. I nonjudgmentally took notice of the progression of these thoughts and gently brought my mind back to my breathing.

With that said, let's turn our attention to how we can incorporate physical activity into our lives for not only the physical benefits, but also the stress reduction benefits they offer us. Some of the physical activities to consider incorporating into your daily lives for stress reduction are as follow:

▶ WALKING: One of my favorite activities when feeling stressed is walking. Walking seems to give me an outlet for not only the psychological changes caused by stressful thoughts when my body begins the fight or flight response, but the activity seems to clear my head, giving me the opportunity to develop better solutions to the problems causing me anxiety. By incorporating walking into your daily life, one finds that it can also allow your body to not have stress buildup because of your daily life activities.

When at home, my own walking routine is done twice during the day. At the end of my workday, I walk to the post office to mail the day's letters generated from promoting my speaking business. My second walk comes during the evening when my wife helps me walk the dogs. This affords us not only an enjoyable physical activity, but an opportunity to spend time daily connecting with what is going on in our individual lives.

While traveling, walking is incorporated into my

daily activities, too. Flying out of the Will Rogers World Airport in Oklahoma City offers me the opportunity to walk from my car, always parked at the north parking lot. It is about a half mile or six to seven minutes of walking following my 2 1/2-hour drive from Mangum to Oklahoma City. It is nice to have that activity before getting on a plane to my destination. It also offers me the opportunity upon returning from my travels to take a walk before driving home. These return flights are usually late in the evening, arriving between 10:00 and 11:00 P.M. This activity helps awaken me for the late night travel home facing me.

When on the road, it is nice to stay in hotels where I can walk to supper and back. This offers me the opportunity to enjoy this activity before and after my evening meal. It also is a nice and different way to see a new city.

About a month ago my travels took me to Boise, Idaho. My speaking ended at 2:00 P.M. local time, and my return flight wasn't until the following day. My afternoon was spent walking to the local art museum, shopping, and choosing a nice local pub for supper. Though the evening was cool and crisp, the memory of this time elicits feelings of pleasure and exhilaration. Much of the beauty of Boise would have been lost if these destinations had been arrived at by cab. Instead, getting to the destination proved to be at least half the fun!

Following a less that optimal program in Topeka, Kansas, a few months ago, the opportunity for a walk helped me relieve feelings of anxiety. While at the Kansas City airport, with about an hour to go before my 10:00 P.M. flight to Oklahoma City, I walked the length of the terminal twice (a distance of close to two miles, taking me thirty minutes). This offered me not only a physical outlet for my anxiety, but afforded me the time to think through the points believed to have gone poorly during the day. As my anxiety about these began to subside, my mind began to review the components of the program that had gone well. Once the perspective changed on this event, the feelings of stress also changed to feelings of gratitude for continued improvement of my programs for future audiences. It is my belief that the activity of walking brought on this change in perspective.

When walking, try to focus your attention on your steps, your breathing, or even the scenery of the environment. This focusing of attention away from the thoughts causing stress will go a long way towards the changing of perspective necessary to change your feelings of stress.

▶ YOGA: Many are moving away from the belief that yoga is a freakish activity only done while high on mind-altering drugs or living in a Buddhist monastery in Tibet. Yoga is more in the mainstream of America than many know. During a layover in the St. Louis airport last week, I watched an older woman doing one of the many yoga movements just to loosen up between flights. It doesn't have to be mysterious or difficult. In fact, it can be fun!

There are many disciplines of yoga out there, but don't let this intimidate you! Yoga can be experienced by finding a yoga center in your area, by video classes, or books. My own yoga routines are really a composite of moves from different yoga practices that seem to offer benefit in my own life. When it comes to stress reduction, the main thing is to do moves that are relaxing and offer the opportunity to focus your attention away from the thoughts causing stress. You should aim for your attention to be focused on the movement and breathing.

▶ DANCING: One of the joys of my life is acting in a local community theater. This endeavor began as an opportunity to be involved in an activity that my daughter, Maggie, wanted to try. As time has passed, it has developed into a love of mine, too. During our last play, *Rumors* by Neil Simon, there was a scene where the cast was trying to develop an alibi for the police, who were knocking on the front door, as to why they had not heard two gunshots during the evening's course of events. It was decided they would turn music on loudly and begin dancing. When the police opened the door, they were faced with six people dancing to Ritchie Valens' *La Bamba*. Being onstage dancing in front of not only my fellow cast members but an audience made me self-conscious.

Most people remember their first high school dance and the anxiety felt when they thought about having to get up in front of peers, dancing to the music. Though the anxiety may be for different reasons between slow and fast dancing, there is anxiety over performing in front of your fellow dance goers. The key here is to overcome your self-consciousness about dancing and feel the movements deep within your body.

When you tap into the authentic movement of the body into music, without the self-consciousness associated with dancing, the results are nothing short of therapeutic. Peg Jordan, R.N., again in her book *Fitness Instinct*, noted that psychiatrist Carl Jung pioneered therapy based upon expressive movement. Ms. Jordan also points out that dancing is a natural energizer and de-stressor.

During the day, try to find times when you can dance. When you feel moved by a particular song, let your body move! This can be in your office, in the airport (not that anyone there is going to see you again), in your living room or in the backyard! My favorite dancing songs include *Paradise* by Meat Loaf, *Gimme Three Steps* by Lynyrd Skynyrd and *Honky Tonk Women* by the greatest rock-and-roll band in the world, the Rolling Stones. When these songs are on, it is difficult for me to remain still, and I let these movements be released!

It is difficult to remain stressed when you get in touch with your body's movement to music and allow it to change your perspective. Not only is the movement important, but the music allows your mind to shift gears from the thoughts that cause stress!

▶ MASSAGE: Many find the word massage conjuring up feelings of deep relaxation void of stress, and this is appropriate. A massage has relaxing benefits, but also physical healing benefits. Research shows us that people receiving a massage have increases in immunoglobulin A within minutes of the massage (immunoglobulin A is an infection-fighting substance), have relaxed muscles, and have increases in the flow of energy and blood flow.

One of the outgrowths of the physical benefits of the massage is a relaxed mind! This relaxing of the mind will also help in changing your perspective on the events that conjure up stressful thoughts within your mind.

The most important aspect of getting into the routine of massage is finding the masseuse who gives you the outcome you are pursuing with the massage. My experience with looking for a masseuse is you must just try them before finding the right one! (My current one, Peggy Booker in Altus, Oklahoma, is wonderful, but it took my trying three others before finding her! She has a firm touch on my muscles and is great company for the hour. Peggy, I love you!)

After finding the appropriate masseuse, the next thing to develop is your routine for a massage. Most recommend having one every two weeks. My own routine is to schedule one every two weeks on Wednesday, Thursday or Saturday as this coincides with my running program. (Massage makes my muscles dead for running purposes, and thus they are scheduled around days when my running will be lighter and slower.) This appointment also gives me the opportunity to drive alone for thirty minutes before and after. This is a perfect opportunity for me to practice new material for my programs or just enjoy the ride!

Once you develop your own massage routine, you may find it to be a necessity for your physical and mental well-being!

▶ GARDENING: Yes, manual labor is a wonderful physical activity for your body and mind. We must work our bodies or they will degenerate from lack of use. The generations that preceded ours usually performed manual labor for their weekly paycheck, but today our jobs are tied more to mental talents instead of a strong back. Think about your grandparents. My mother's parents ate pork, gravy, sweets, etc., but they lived to be into their eighties and nineties. Though they did not have a structured exercise program, they worked on the farm, performing manual labor on a daily basis.

Many have found the physical activity of gardening and yard work to be of great physical and mental benefit. Twyla loves nothing more that getting outside to work in the soil. She plants a small garden, tends to the flowers in our front yard, and mows the lawn as more of a mental recharging exercise than a necessary chore to be performed. Thankfully for the residents of Mangum, Oklahoma, Twyla enjoys mowing. If it were left up to me, the task would never be completed as mowing is, in my opinion, a hideous activity. This attitude seems to be passed down to me genetically as my great-grandfather rarely mowed his lawn. When asked when he was going to mow, he would respond that the frost would be upon them in only four months, so he didn't think it was necessary to mow at that time!

When you perform manual labor such as yard work, not only are you reconnecting with the earth, you are focusing your attention on the task at hand, changing your perspective on the events that conjure up stressful thoughts within your mind, plus you have beauty to show for it! As the potter will tell you, the end product is not the goal, it is immersing oneself in the activity.

▶ NATURE: Whether you walk, run, practice yoga or participate in any other physical activity, one of the decisions you have to make is where to do the activity. Doing physical activity in the gym has advantages, including a moderation of temperature, an environment safe from automobiles and people who may wish to harm you, and the company of people performing similar activities. There is nothing quite as wonderful as doing your activity outdoors.

Thomas Lenord says nature can teach us many things, including how to slow down, be more patient, creative, persistent, and how to go with the flow. Nature also teaches us to not always insist on our own way, to find alternatives rather than try to push. Natures shows us there is a natural order to the universe, that the cold winter always follows colors of fall and precedes the flowers of spring. What a wonderful sentiment.

It is difficult the determine, but it is my personal opinion that a great deal of the benefit of physical activity comes from communing with the earth and the environment outside. Walking on the beach while feeling the sand between your toes, gazing at the stars through a clear, crisp Oklahoma sky, being in the company of trees as the leaves are beginning to change colors signaling the beginning of the fall season, watching a sunrise over a frosty winter landscape or a sunset on the ocean after a beautiful summer day are all therapy offered by meditation with nature. Even without activity, the earth offers countless opportunities to renew your spirit and body through interaction with it. Take time to enjoy the outdoors, regardless of the activity or lack of it.

Even if you are not engaged in physical activity, it is nice to commune with the great outdoors.

Should you want to begin or maintain a more structured program of physical activity to increase your fitness and overall physical and emotional well-being, please see Appendix A.

Physical activity will:

- Allow your body to release hormones known as endorphins, a natural pain killer and antidepressant.

- Focus your attention away from the thoughts that continue to cause you the feelings of stress.

- Give your body an outlet for the psychological changes caused by stressful thoughts when your body begins the fight or flight response.

- Improve your self-image, all of which will help you ***Let It Go, Just Let It Go!***

Chapter 7

Relationships

---

amy has a softball game thursday afternoon
tom needs braces the dentist says
she clears the table
he puts dishes in the washer

she asks him to balance the checkbook
he asks her to mail some letters
they wish each other good day
quick kisses, one hug

he thinks she is heavier
sometimes solemn
still a good woman, mostly pleasant
she thinks he is heavier, keeps things in
still a good man, likes him around

she folds dry towels
whispers thank you
he stops at a light
whispers thank you.

—*Epiphanies* by Dan Quisenberry from *On Days Like This*

As I start on this chapter, my cat is sitting on my desk playing with one of my Pentels. She is my companion during the days at home, and she likes to help me in the office. She knows she can do no wrong in my eyes and is pretty much allowed to do whatever her heart desires. Sit on my papers on my desk? Sure. Knock my Pentel off the desk and break the lead? Why not? Walk on the fax machine and mess up the setting so it doesn't work? Well, yes, that is allowed as well. Why? Because she brings me great comfort during both good times and bad.

When we are having a bad day at the office, my princess offers me the same unconditional love and warmth as when things are going well. When we don't get an engagement we have been counting on, she is there. When my finances are lacking, she is there. When the writing isn't going well, she is there. She does funny things like drag stuffed animals and a coonskin cap from my daughter's upstairs bedroom to the office, engage in quite a battle for some sort of transgression she has seen them perform, then ends the episode by giving them a bath. When she is told no, she looks at me like, "You don't understand, I'm a princess and do just as I please!" As I cuddle and gently caress her head, it is difficult to experience the thoughts causing the stresses of my day.

I am reminded of the closing paragraph of a book I read a few years ago. *Are You Somebody, The Accidental Memoir of a Dublin Woman* by Nuala O'Faolain closes with the following:

> *To be just myself, like the cat, which is so perfectly and unself-consciously a cat and does not know it will perish. What can I do, when everything is so various and so beyond me, but cling on, and thank the God I don't believe in for the miracles showered on me?*

My relationship with my cat offers me joy during the good times and comfort during the times of distress. That is what relationships do for us, regardless of what type of sentient being the relationship is with. They are there so we don't have to travel the journey of life alone. They offer us the pillow of comfort when we are distressed, the ear of listening when we need to talk, the voice of reason when we are blinded by our thoughts of situations, and the punch line of the joke when we need to laugh at the situation. Yes, we were meant to journey though this life together.

Early this year a kind of call that we all dread came to the office. My mother informed me that one of my uncles had been killed in an accident at work. It felt as if the breath of life had been sucked right out of my body. My uncle, Bobby, was a gentle man and a kind man, one I looked up to and admired for as long as my mind possesses memories. My daughter had just gotten home from school and, when I told her what had happened, she offered comfort and assurance to me. It dawned on me during the trip to Missouri for Bobby's funeral that Maggie was growing up, and a smile crossed my face as I envisioned the numerous times in the future she will have to accept the burden during difficult times by offering her father and mother comfort. To this day, when my thoughts return to the horror of that call from my mom, I also remember how my daughter stepped up to comfort me.

How do we develop quality relationships with our family, friends, and pets? This chapter will offer you what my experience and study has taught me, but the first point to be made is that there are no "normal" relationships. Don't think you need to model your relationships after anyone else, nor do you need to compare your relationships to those of others. It has been my experience that all relationships are different and, as long as it meets the needs of both parties, that is what it should be. Let your relationships be unique, just as they were intended to be.

Twyla and I have been married a long time! Being an accountant by training, I am naturally rather anal retentive. In our relationship, my mind naturally remembers dates and schedules better than Twyla. A couple of years ago in late February, I was doing two days of engagements in Tampa, Florida. Twyla called me one evening in my hotel room and asked, "Now tell me again, when is our anniversary?" I told her it was March 1 and you could hear a sigh of relief on the other end of the receiver. Twyla then asked me how many years we had been married? Have you ever had that dream you were taking a test that you hadn't studied for? That was the feeling which rippled through my mind as I calculated our marriage duration. When it was determined we had been married fifteen years, Twyla responded, "It just seems like yesterday that we got married."

My how that flattered me. My response was, "Twyla,

I believe that may be the nicest thing anyone has ever said to me." She immediately followed my comment with, "And you know what a rotten day yesterday was!"

Like any relationship of the duration of ours, we have had good times and bad times. During one of the more difficult times, we read a book by Phillip C. McGraw, Ph.D., called *Relationship Rescue*. Four ideas garnered from this book have helped me tremendously. Keeping these present in my attitudes with my relationships, especially the one with Twyla, seem to have improved my conduct within these relationships and subsequently the relationships themselves. These are as follow:

- Always let the relationship transcend the turmoil of our daily lives.
- Always build up the other person's self-esteem.
- Remember to remain friends.
- Remember the reasons why I fell in love with this person.

All of our lives are filled with daily turmoil which, in the overall scheme of life, matters little. As I allowed my relationships to transcend this turmoil, I eliminated many of the petty fights and concerns that used to sidetrack me from day to day. When your life ends, the money problems, minor issues with your children, work-related problems, laundry, meals, dirty dishes, the cat's litter box, etc., matter little. When you remember this on a daily basis, your relationship will naturally be a more smooth and prosperous one.

During your interactions with your loved ones, always build up their self-esteem. Research tells us that people with high self-esteem are naturally more happy, successful, and healthier. Research also tells us that people with high self-esteem know that the important people in their lives, including parents, children and employers, love them, as well as that they possess all of the skills necessary in order to be successful in their lives. When you are conversing with your spouse or children, remember to help them understand that you love them and that they have all the skills necessary in order to be a success in their lives.

The third one has more to do with your relationship with your spouse, but it can apply to all relationships. Remember to remain friends. Remembering the early days of my relationship with Twyla, my actions were more intended on friendship than lovers. We engaged in conversations to get to know each other better, we supported each other during difficult times, and had a genuine interest in what each other was doing, feeling, and thinking. Too often the natural experience of being together for a long time will dull that friendship. When you make a conscious effort to be friends, you find many of the original benefits of the relationship will return.

Finally, remember why you fell in love with the person in the first place. Often we fall in love with people who have different qualities than we possess. When we have been in a relationship for a long time, we find these differences begin to get on our nerves. When we remember these were the qualities that we fell in love with in the first place, we can begin to surpass the pettiness of those feelings. Twyla is very creative, both artistically and with thought. She seems to live more fully in the present moment, she has little pretense, what you see with her is what you get, and she has a great sense of humor. Over the years, some of these qualities have been the same thing that have driven me crazy within our relationship, but when I remember how wonderful these qualities are, my impatience with her melts away.

A few months ago, my speaking took me away from home for nine days. During this trip, I was going to have to wire some money for a business deal, and knew I had some checks coming to the office that would cover this wire. When I left home, I left a very detailed note for Twyla regarding four checks that were coming in the mail, including the client name, the dollar amount, and the expected date of the checks. Being an anal-retentive accountant, there were even four deposit slips stapled to the note so she wouldn't even have to make a decision regarding the account into which they needed to be deposited. All she had to do was put the amount of the check on the deposit slip and take it to the bank a half mile from our house.

During the first few days of the trip, Twyla told me all four checks had arrived and she had taken them to the bank. On the eighth day of the trip I called the bank and gave them the wiring instructions. When this was done, the teller asked me where the money for this wire was coming from. I told her from my business account. She informed me there wasn't enough money in the account. Knowing there should be plenty there, we began to investigate the deposits which had been made in my absence. She had the last two deposits made by Twyla, but was missing the first two. She checked my personal account, the night depository, even looking through all the deposits of that day to see if the money had been put in anyone else's account. The two deposits were no where to be found. Before speaking that evening, I called Twyla and asked her if she was sure she made the deposits. A terse response of yes was received!

When the engagement that evening was completed, my journey continued with another flight and another hotel. Upon getting settled into my new room, I called Twyla at home, again inquiring about the deposits. She said the bank must have screwed up, as she was sure they had been made. During the flight home and my 2 1/2-hour drive from the Oklahoma City airport to Mangum, my anger had taken center stage. My thoughts of having to take a day off the following week to call the clients about stopping payment of the checks and getting reissued checks filled me with indignation.

Upon my entry into our house, I was met by my son. He had just received brand new red baseball cleats for his upcoming season. His pride was evident by the look on his face, but my anger blinded me to this. My mature comment of "Well, who is going to pay for those since I don't have any money?" turned his joy instantly to dejection.

My fourteen-year-old daughter, hearing the opening

comment to her brother, said to me, "Dad, I don't want you to bring up the deposit situation to Mom. She is very upset by it."

I looked at her and said, "She is upset? She is upset? What does she have to be upset about? I will have to be the one to take Monday off to call the clients about getting new checks issued and stop payment on the old ones. If anyone has the right to be upset, it is me!"

She simply looked at me and said, "I'm telling you, for your own good, you shouldn't bring this situation up."

Her advice was not taken as I opened my conversation with Twyla that night by saying, "A fifty percent success rate, though great in baseball, really stinks at getting deposits from our house to the bank a half mile away!" As you can imagine, our conversation went downhill after that comment, and we engaged in one of the worst conflicts of our married life.

To this day, my handling of this situation incites great shame within me. First of all, my actions and comments that evening weren't those of someone who allows his relationship transcend the turmoil in his life. Yes, it would have fallen on me to take the day off on Monday to call the clients about stopping payment on their checks and reissuing them (the original checks were found the following day by Twyla in her car even though both of us had made thorough checks of the cars), but that is of little consequence in the overall scheme of our lives!

Though that should be enough, my worst shame is felt at my lack of building up Twyla's self-esteem with this situation. My heart broke that evening when she commented, "I feel like I'm not even smart enough to get deposits to the bank!"

Twyla, on the other hand, seems to consistently exude these four traits. I have known no one who consistently maintains her focus on the important aspects of life like Twyla. She does not let the day-to-day problems creep into her actions with me, the children, or her performance as a public school art teacher. She seems to be able to decide instantly if a situation is critical in nature and, if not, allow it to pass without another thought.

When she deals with me or our children, she constantly seems to be building up our self-esteem. When my mother-in-law had about six weeks to live, she and I went for a walk in the yard one hot Sunday afternoon. Emma Lou told me she was very proud of our children and complimented Twyla and me for doing such a good job rearing them. I quite honestly admitted that the thanks needed to go to Twyla because what few positive parenting skills I knew I had learned from her. I believe her finest skill when it comes to our children is that she is always building up their self-esteem, even when addressing a problem with them. She continually addresses the behavior, while maintaining the child's self-esteem.

Twyla and I were friends a long time before we were lovers, companions, or husband and wife. To this day, she and I remain each other's best friend. In fact, during our difficult times it has been compounded because the person causing her heartache and misery is her best friend. She and

I often said that it was difficult to experience marital trouble not because of the threat to the marriage, but because we felt inhibited to tell our best friend they were hurting us as a husband or wife. We have also said that, even if our marriage ended, we wanted to remain friends. This was what our relationship was first built on and want we most treasure about it.

At the program in Amarillo where Twyla told me I did not make an appearance in her wildest dreams, she sat in the audience, as she usually does, without anyone knowing she is my wife. During the program, after telling the audience that Twyla possessed no concept of time, the lady sitting next to Twyla leaned over to her and said, "You know, I don't know why she puts up with him." To this day, that is one of the funniest comments I have ever heard!

It is my opinion the best quality Twyla possesses with regard to our relationship is that she remembers daily why she fell in love with me and accepts, unconditionally, the faults which I possess without letting them upset her too much. The compulsiveness, the constant competitiveness, my obsessive behaviors, the quick Irish temper, even the fact that I am very selfish when it comes to my career and time. Though these are behaviors she doesn't enjoy or, in some cases, even understand, she knows they are part of the package that is Kent, and she accepts them because she finds the reasons she fell in love with me to outweigh the ones that drive her crazy.

Here are just a few points I have found to be helpful in keeping these principles fresh in your relationships. You may want to try these for yourself.

- I am presented with a situation with my loved ones that upsets me. Instead of just blowing off, I try to take a minute to remember a similar situation in the past, like the deposit story, where my actions caused pain and resentment. When I remember the shame and self-deprecation I experienced following it, this allows me the opportunity to be more mindful in discussing the problem with my family. I still fail today but not at the same rate as I used to.

- Go for a walk when you get angry with your loved ones and have time to change your perspective on the situation.

- I keep a prayer book with me. It is a book of quotations and things I find inspirational that I have picked up along the way. I read something from there daily as soon as I finish my morning pages. It reminds me of the important things in my life, especially my family, and keeps them more in my thoughts during the day.

- Take time to be with your family members without the television or other distractions. My time with Twyla is during the first few minutes of her day. I get up between 4:00 and 5:00 A.M., write, drink coffee, read, and generally prepare for my day. Twyla isn't a morning person. Her alarm goes off at 6:30 A.M., but she takes her time waking up. I return to our bedroom and spend that time with her. I cherish this time, and it is the thing I miss the most about home when I have to travel.

My time with the children is usually spent playing sports. Keith and I still play catch, though not as much now that he is driving and has other things in his life. Maggie and I play basketball (she cheats), play catch, and walk the dogs at night.

▶ Do something for your family without expecting them to reciprocate. Fix them a meal or take them out for a meal, call unexpectedly during the day, write a quick note, or purchase a small gift. Doing something nice for someone without wanting anything in return can be a wonderful gift indeed.

▶ Have time away from your daily routine. Even if it is just going out for a hamburger together. Twyla and I try to have some time away every year together, but sometimes the best times are when we just go shopping together. Following an engagement in Tulsa, we took some time to do some window shopping, then had time in the car driving home.

Relationships require a great deal of work and discipline. They not only provide you with a refuge for situations you find that cause you stress, but they often give focus to your relationship and put situations into their proper perspective. When you invest yourself fully in the relationship, you realize how petty and unimportant many of your daily situations are in reference to your life. As your relationships become paramount, you will find you are better able to ***Let It Go, Just Let It Go!***

CHAPTER 8

Compassion

Compassion can be roughly defined in terms of a state of mind that is nonviolent, non-harming, and nonaggressive. It is a mental attitude based on the wish for others to be free of their suffering and is associated with a sense of commitment, responsibility, and respect towards others.

—His Holiness The Dalai Lama
from *The Art of Happiness*

When the decision was made to transition my career from accounting to being a professional speaker and author, I didn't want to take a dramatic cut in my income. The logical choice was to continue to do accounting work, while simultaneously pursuing a career in speaking and writing. For the first two years of speaking, my income was supplemented with accounting work. As my revenue from speaking increased, I was able to reduce the number of accounting clients utilizing my services.

At the end of the second year of being on my own, my accounting practice encompassed two bookkeeping clients, both of whom knew our days of working together were limited. At that time, though, I found myself embroiled in a fight with the executive director of the State Board of Accountancy regarding the need for me to have a permit to practice public accounting for two bookkeeping clients! We argued over something which appears to be clearly outlined in the state accountancy act. (In fact, the attorneys at the state capital who wrote the law said my opinion was clearly correct, but the State Board of Accountancy had absolute authority on how they could interpret this law. The only way to win this situation was to challenge it in district court and possibly the Oklahoma Supreme Court, a process which would cost tens of thousands of dollars.) My relationship with the director of the State Board of Accountancy was hostile and confrontational from the beginning. In fact, at one point I told the director that she should do whatever she thought she had the power to do to me, but I wasn't playing her stupid game anymore. She spent the next three months showing me how much power she actually could exert over me.

My case was sent to a hearing at the office of the State Board of Accountancy in Oklahoma City, presided over by a representative of the attorney general's office, then on to prosecution by the State Board of Accountancy. It was eventually settled after great turmoil with me having my C.P.A. certificate suspended for one year and paying $2,500 in prosecution costs. Apparently using the words gestapo, mafia and extortion aren't as funny to them as they were to me.

My feelings of hopelessness, anger and betrayal hardened into bitterness. Bitterness toward this woman who personified the organization and behavior which, in my opinion, were wrong. I allowed these feelings to continue throughout the duration of the situation. On the day the consent order was to be signed, a magical thing happened to me.

As I signed my name to a document saying I was guilty of something which I continued to believe wasn't right, my bitterness began to rise again. With the paper signed and sealed in the return envelope, it was placed in the outgoing mail of the day. My daily routine is to walk to the post office a mile from our house with the outgoing mail. This day was a beautiful, spring, Oklahoma afternoon with a pleasant temperature, low humidity and a clear, blue sky overhead. My bitterness became replaced with enjoyment of such a beautiful afternoon and my daily physical activity of walking to the post office.

As my journey continued, my thoughts turned to the memory of the working conditions of those in the State Board of Accountancy. They slave daily in a lightless state office in a lifeless state office building. The director was a middle-aged woman who seemed to have a scowl permanently ingrained on her face. As my memory of sitting in that place continued, I realized not only how fortunate I was to earn a living doing something I love, but that it does not have to be in an environment such as hers. How antagonistic, contentious, and even hostile would my behavior be if it were me having to do her job? When people dislike their job, it does seem to infect the remainder of their life. If my job entailed doing something that seems to have little social value, my attitude certainly would be as hateful as hers.

My compassion in that moment began to replace my feelings of stress and anger with feelings of empathy for her! By putting myself in her position, my view on this situation changed from how it affected me to what is the real importance of this anyway. It doesn't affect my ability to earn a living; it only places a black mark on my accounting career, which will probably not be returned to in the future.

How can compassion help with stressful feelings?

This is one that you may not have expected, but cultivating compassion is helpful during stressful times. It is one that I must work on daily and, take it from me, it takes great patience in order to develop. In the beginning of this book it was pointed out that stress is an emotional reaction to our stressful thoughts about situations we believe to be stressful. A point overlooked here is that our perspective on events is usually from the point of view of how these events affect us!

Yes, we are a selfish breed. Before you get down on yourself, realize this is a natural human condition within all of us. Compassion for another's point of view is not a natural process, but one that can be cultivated with work and mindfulness. We all view life from our own perspective, and it takes effort to change that perspective to that of another person. When you begin to cultivate compassion, especially during situations with others which you find stressful, you may find great benefit to yourself and the other person.

Where do we find compassion and how does it help us reduce our stress? A few years ago the Minnesota Chamber of Commerce asked me to do a program regarding the positive financial and social impacts of environmentally conscious practices. During the preparation of this program, the research pointed out how our whole world is interdependent and interconnected! A prime example is the interdependence of our bodies and plants. Our bodies breath oxygen and emit carbon dioxide as a waste product. Trees and plants take in carbon dioxide and emit as a waste product oxygen. We can't survive without trees and plants, and vice versa.

In fact, much of our world has intricate examples of interdependence and interconnectedness. We are not only dependent upon nonhuman aspects of our world, we are dependent upon other people as well. Where would any of us be without the nurturing of our mothers? Without them, we would have died in just a few hours or days of our birth. I think one of the exciting aspects of each of us in our existence as a person is that the same people who we were totally dependent upon when we were born become dependent upon us when they reach their advanced ages! Oh, how life moves in circles.

Where would any of us be without our families? What would the quality of your life be like without your friends? Think of how much joy your pets bring into your life. What about co-workers? How would the quality of our lives be different without them, even the ones that are consistently a pain?

If you really believe you are completely independent and self-sufficient in this world, consider a Tibetan meal prayer. It opens by thanking the "seventy-two laborers" who brought the food to us. Think about it the next time you are sitting down to eat a meal. There were people who planted the vegetables, and raised the animals which provided the meat, not to mention the animal which gave its life for the meal (I mentioned this once at a meal of ours and my son, who has always exhibited a high degree of sensitivity, began crying about the chicken who had lost its life for his meal!). There were people involved in growing the food for the animals to eat, people who harvested the food, packaged it, even transported it to the store for us to purchase. Still others were involved in selling and purchasing the food to get it to our local grocery store, people at the store to place it on the shelves, the checkout people when we purchase it, and the ones who prepare the meal. Even after we eat, there are those who clean the table and dishes, and still others who dispose of the waste of packaging and the leftovers.

Before you become too smug about being self-sufficient, think about how long would you exist if you had to do all that by yourself just to eat. Then think of having to eat two to three times per day! It does get you thinking about how we are all dependent upon each other for our existence.

As we understand that our life is intricately tied closely to others, we begin to better understand compassion.

We must further understand two basic facts about life. The first is we individually see events and situations from how they affect us. When you are presented with a situation, your first thoughts are "how does this affect me?" One of my favorite shows on television used to be "Murphy Brown." She exhibited the selfishness that I too often see in myself and find humor in having pointed out to me. Once when she was talking with one of her coworkers, she said, "You don't understand. If it doesn't affect me, it isn't important." We all have more of Murphy Brown in us than we would care to admit!

The second aspect of human existence we must acknowledge is all people basically want the same thing from their lives. We all have many of the same fears, joys, dreads and problems. It is often pointed out to me that everyone loves their children and wants the best for them. Most of us have monthly bills that must be paid, and we struggle with our jobs, our spouses, and our parents from time to time. Though we may handle the pressures of these situations differently, we all seem to possess many of the same situations that may cause feelings of stress.

When you begin to realize that we are all interdependent and interconnected in this world, that we analyze situations from our own point of view, and that everyone here has the same basic needs, desires, and fears, we can begin to soften our actions and thoughts naturally. Phil Jackson, in his book *Sacred Hoops: Spiritual Lessons of a Hardwood Warrior*, states that he follows what he calls "compassionate leadership." He is quoted as saying, "What you do to others, you do to yourself and what you do to yourself, you do to the others. When you show the same care and respect for others that you show for yourself, you will begin to see we all share the same basic human struggles, desires and dreams. With this awareness, the barriers between people begin to come down and we begin to develop understanding, patience and compassion."

Daily actions of compassion can redirect your thoughts from your own stressful events. When your mind is occupied with thoughts of compassion toward others, your mind cannot be occupied with thoughts of stress. Though this alone is a positive enough reason to offer compassion to others, there are other reasons for developing compassion. You help others! What more noble pursuit could we engage in as residents of the community of earth? For a moment, think of the last time someone helped you. Didn't you feel really wonderful because of their care and concern? Didn't it renew your faith in humankind? Didn't your appreciation for them overflow?

Also, as you help others, aren't you filled with positive feelings? Think about the last time you helped someone less fortunate than yourself. Didn't you receive positive feelings from those actions? Weren't you offered the glow that comes from loving others? This can be one of the most rewarding pursuits in and of itself.

With the preceding aspects noted, we can begin to develop compassion. Richard Carlson, in *Don't Sweat the Small Stuff and It's All Small Stuff,* states we must have two components in developing compassion. These are intention and action. Intention is simply remembering that offering compassion to others is important, as is consciously trying to see things from another's perspective. Our intentions are not enough, we must take action on our compassion.

During the summer between my junior and senior year at William Jewell College, I needed to take a humanities course. The two choices were ethics, offered in the library, and world religions, offered in Jewell Hall. Since my apartment didn't have air-conditioning, the choice was easy as the library was air-conditioned and Jewell Hall wasn't. I enrolled in ethics before the other summer students figured out this benefit.

One of the lessons taught in this class was the Christian's "Golden Rule." One of the points that stood out for me was that Christ wanted us to treat others the way we would want to be treated, not so our treatment would be good in return. Christ wanted us to treat others as we would want to be treated simply for the intent that we should love everyone. This ties directly to our intention to show compassion to others. It should not be for selfish reasons, but so we can actually make others' lives easier and more enjoyable.

The old saying "The road to hell is paved with good intentions" certainly holds true here. Having the intention to offer compassion isn't enough. It must be followed by action.

As action is implemented, it need not be complex, elaborate, or painful. Dr. Carlson points out it can be as simple as "a beautiful smile and genuine 'hello' to the people you meet on the street." Though we may want to elaborate on our compassionate actions, these are also effective in helping others and yourself.

His Holiness the Dalai Lama, in the book *The Art of Happiness,* offers us good insight on how to develop compassion for others. The Dalai Lama points out that empathy is an important factor in developing compassion for others. Making the effort to appreciate another's suffering by putting yourself in their position can help you develop compassion for that person. The Dalai Lama says practicing empathy when presented with any sentient being who is suffering will help one develop the tools necessary to be able to experience empathy when presented with a confrontation or a stressful situation.

Maggie decided two years ago she wanted to be a cheerleader. If your daughter ever decides to be a cheerleader you will get a note from the cheerleader sponsor which states she wants to have a meeting with the cheerleaders and the moms. I want to warn everyone, the note truly means the moms. The cheerleader sponsor doesn't need us dads there.

Twyla had parent-teacher conferences on the night of this meeting and I thought to myself, "How hard can this be?" I decided I would go to the meeting with Maggie.

When I arrived there were eight fourteen-year-old girls, seven moms, and a female cheerleading sponsor. The meeting was about the uniforms these girls were going to wear the following year. Have you noticed those uniforms lately? The cheerleading sponsor had a catalog with pictures of the uniforms they were considering, all with a short, revealing skirt that I was not sure I wanted my daughter wearing in public.

I do a program for schools about developing a collaborative environment and one of the items I discuss is not being afraid to be different, so I thought I should apply it in this situation. I said, "Hey, let's not be afraid to be different. Wouldn't it be cool if we got ankle length skirts?" Everyone in the room looked at me like I had lost my mind. Maggie leaned over to me and whispered, "Would you just shut up."

The discussion turned to the uniforms the girls were getting to wear at camp that summer. The sponsor went into elaborate detail about these, including the undergarments the girls were going to wear. Now I am not very comfortable talking about my own undergarments, let alone my daughter's.

The sponsor said, "We are going to wear a white jog bra under this top, a black jog bra under this top, and a gold jog bra under this one."

The mom at the far end of the table said, "You know, I don't think I have ever seen a gold jog bra."

The mom sitting to my left said, "You know, I don't think I have ever seen a gold bra at all."

Like an idiot I said, "Well, I have."

Now I have a female cheerleading sponsor, seven moms, and eight fourteen-year-old girls, including my daughter who knows mommy doesn't have a gold bra at home, wanting to know where I saw it. I was never filled with so much empathy for what Twyla goes through as at that moment.

Besides placing yourself in another's shoes, the Dalai Lama believes empathy can be developed by looking for similarities between yourself and others. He states, "Whenever I meet people I always approach them from the standpoint of the most basic things we have in common. We each have a physical structure, a mind, emotions. We are all born in the same way, and we all die. All of us want happiness and do not want to suffer. Looking at others from this standpoint rather than emphasizing secondary differences such as the fact that I am Tibetan, or a different color, religion, or cultural background, allows me to have a feeling that I'm meeting someone just the same as me. I find that relating to others on that level makes it much easier to exchange and communicate with one another."

When you are involved with a stressful situation with someone, can you take a moment to realize the similarities between the two of you instead of the differences? When you do, you see that person as yourself, and it helps bring about a change in perspective on the events.

Finally, there is a meditation practice known as "tong len" (pronounced "tong-len"). This meditation is quite literally known as the "Sending-and-Taking" meditation because we send love and compassion to others and try to take their suffering on ourselves. What parent isn't pained when they see their own children being hurt? There are very few parents who wouldn't take the place of their child who is in pain in order to help the child feel better. This is what we are wanting to do with this meditation. We want to send love and compassion to those who are hurting and try to accept their pain and suffering upon ourselves.

Lama Surya Das describes this practice in his book, *Awakening the Buddha Within,* as follows:

> *Tonglen—literally known as Sending-and-Taking—is an integral part of the Mahayana mind-training. Some Westerners balk at the practice of tonglen because they tend to take it too literally. They don't see it as what it is: a way of transforming the recalcitrant hardened heart into a heart softened by love and empathy. My suggestion is: Don't be afraid of it; rather, regard it initially as an advanced mind-training technique to be used as a way of increasing one's capacity for unconditional love, generosity, and openness of heart. When you are ready to undertake such selfless practice, it awaits you.*
>
> *Tonglen—the taking on of burdens without feeling burdened—is a lesson in letting go of self-clinging and attachment, and transforming egotism into love. For centuries the learned practitioners of Tibet have used sending-and-taking as a way of freeing up, loosening up, and dissolving the barriers between self and others by transforming self-centered attitudes. For example, if you are in the middle of an acrimonious situation, don't expect tonglen to fix it on the spot, but it can help you change your point of view and, in the process, change the entire atmosphere.*
>
> *One is asked to approach this Sending-and-Taking meditation with an attitude of extraordinary compassion and love for all. Think about all the suffering in the world.*

Wouldn't it be wonderful to be able to take pain and convert it to happiness, health, and well-being? Wouldn't it be a worthwhile thing if you could open your heart, accepting suffering and being able to transform it into love and goodness?

This meditation begins by offering acceptance and love to yourself. Too often we treat others much more kindly than we treat ourselves. We find their human frailties to be forgivable, but not our own. We are human beings deserving of love and compassion, especially from ourselves. As you offer yourself compassion and love, you will find the pain of the past or present melt away.

Once you have offered acceptance to yourself, you then move to those whom you love. Think of your spouse, your children, your parents, those friends who are very close to you! What pain are they experiencing at the current time? Send them thoughts, feelings and prayers of joy and happiness. As you send them comfort, try to accept some of the suffering they are currently experiencing. Though you may not be able to totally accept their suffering, you may be delighted to find they actually feel some of the burden of these situations lifting from their shoulders. (There is more to this world that we don't understand than what we actually do understand. Besides, what could it hurt?)

Finally, you picture those who you dislike, those who have hurt you, wronged you, even slandered you. You are going to offer them compassion, love and happiness, and try to accept their pain. This is a very difficult practice to develop, but one that helps in softening your negative feelings toward these individuals. When you offer those that you dislike compassion and happiness, while trying to lighten the burden of their pain, you may find yourself understanding these people more and being able to offer them the forgiveness that is necessary for your own internal healing.

The first time I read about this practice was early in the morning in a hotel room in Tulsa, Oklahoma, a few years ago. My career was still in accounting exclusively, and my employer was based in Tulsa. My job required me to be in the office about once a month. This office was one of the most tense environments ever established in the business world and most of it, in my opinion, was the result of the managing partner. My attitude would begin deteriorating upon my arrival in the hotel in Tulsa. The practice of Tonglen seemed to offer an opportunity to help with my attitude about having to enter this tense environment, but it had quite an unexpected turn later in the morning.

My practice that morning began by offering love and compassion to myself. My faults and mistakes of recent time were taken into consideration and offered a hint of forgiveness. Next, my attention turned toward Twyla. We were experiencing a difficult time in our relationship and, though we argued about situations, I realized that these situations caused her great pain and resentment. My mind tried to take on her pain, and offer her joy and happiness. When this was completed, my heart and mind felt better than it had in months. I was hopeful Twyla was experiencing some of the same sense of relief.

Following this, I went for my morning run in La Fortune Park across the street from the hotel. On this morning, my attention was diverted during my run to the sound of a siren of an ambulance leaving a nearby hospital. My mind was drawn to the fact that, though I was enjoying a nice run after my morning ritual of writing and reading, someone in the near vicinity was in pain. My thoughts went out to not only the individual in physical distress, but to the family members and friends to whom this situation would bring pain.

My thoughts further moved to sending these individuals my positive feelings generated from the wonderful morning experienced by me in the hotel room, plus I tried to take on their pain, trying to allow some of their suffering to my being. My body was strong, my mind free of stress and suffering, so maybe the pain would be absorbed by me easier than by them. These thoughts continued during the remainder of my workout and during the day as the memory of the ambulance's siren would present itself. Did these thoughts help? Well, it will never be known, but it didn't hurt them, and it offered me the positive feelings of trying to help someone through a painful situation. Besides, my day at the Tulsa office went more smoothly than during previous visits.

When compassion is developed during stressful situations via putting yourself in someone else's shoes, you will find it not only changes your perspective of the situation so your thoughts are not on the situation, but will also open up your heart to understanding another's stressful thoughts.

This will help you in not only cultivating relationships with others, but it will also allow you to ***Let It Go, Just Let It Go!***

Let It Go—Just Let It Go!

Chapter 9

Other Ideas

Your teacher can open the door, but
you must enter by yourself.

—Chinese proverb

The chapters that have preceded this are about activities and ideas that I have engaged in which have offered benefits for helping change my perspective with regard to situations I find stressful. In this chapter, I want to offer other ideas that people have been kind enough to share with me.

What all of these have in common are they are activities in which the person involved enjoys partaking. The activities change the person's perspective on situations, thus, changes the person's thoughts with regard to situations and, in turn, changes the person's feelings on the situation. In some cases, the activities may be improving the person's mood, thus having the same effect on the person's feelings.

What I hope this chapter will do is prompt you to begin thinking about activities you enjoy, even if you have not engaged in them in recent years. As I stated earlier, there are no quick fixes when it comes to stress reduction, but one of the resolves you may do to help with this is by committing to take time for yourself.

▶ My good friend, author, and southern humorist, Michael Johnson loves roping calves. He says his uncles taught him at an early age, and he has loved the activity ever since. In his book *Cowboys and Angels*, Michael says the following:

I can remember very clearly, however, when they taught me how to throw a rope. Two of them took me down to the river. They had me throw rocks in the water for some time. I must have been seven or eight years old. I threw rocks for a time, and then one of my uncles handed me the coils of a rope in one hand, and the loop he had built in the other. He told me to throw the loop in the water just as I had thrown the rock. "Same motion," he said, "Just like a rock in the river. That's the way you throw a rope."

Soon, Michael found he became quite proficient at throwing the "lariat" as he said his uncles called it, and the rope actually became an extension of his arm. To this day, he loves nothing more than being on the back of a horse, chasing a calf with the express goal of putting it on the ground and tying it up. Michael not only spends his days at his ranch outside of Idabel, Oklahoma, roping, he continues to compete in roping events around the country.

In talking with Michael, he tells me he enters into a mental zone or flow, much like I experience during my runs. Michael has told me, when he is roping, he becomes one with the horse and the rope, while all are working towards the goal of putting the calf on the ground. This activity changes Michael's perspective on situations in his life, thus changing his feelings of stress, though I bet it increases the stressful feelings for the calf.

▶ Michael Rader, my older brother has had two passions in his life. The first is the railroad, and the second is the stock market. His career has taken him to railroads, a difficult industry because of the economic circumstances and competition faced by those involved. I worry about the stress level that Michael seems to have much of the time, but he loves what he does.

When Michael first graduated from college, he thought he would try being a stockbroker full-time. He passed the SEC exam and entered the world of trading. He found that was not his calling, but his love for the market has remained.

Michael spends his evenings researching and trading his own stock portfolio. I often equate trading in today's stock market to shooting craps in a casino, but Michael is unlike most amateur traders. He spends countless hours watching the trends of the stocks, understanding what is happening to the industry, reviewing the history of the company, even investigating the leadership of an organization to see if they are making decisions that are conducive to the company.

Michael uses the trading of stocks as an activity to cope with the feelings of stress. For whatever reason, he finds this changes his perspective on the events of the day, thus changing his feelings. He'd probably be the first to warn you to not try this at home unless you research the organization in a systematic manner.

▶ My good friend, Wayne McClure, loves hunting for deer and turkey. The joy of this seems less to do with the actual kill than the preparation for the hunt, as well as time spent in nature. Wayne hunts in Missouri every November for deer, and sometimes he comes away from his five-day hunt without anything, but he rarely seems disappointed.

He gears up for this trip months in advance. He spends time sighting his gun just right, stocking and packing his travel trailer, scouting the grounds, picking out the place for his stand, and setting up the stand. All are enjoyable activities of the hunt for him.

I'm sure the time Wayne spends preparing and hunting helps change his perspective on events he finds stressful in his life. In changing his perspective, he changes his thoughts and, thus, his feelings of stress.

▶ One of my favorite people in the world, Mona Chapman, loves making crafts out of wood. She doesn't do these for profit but for the activity. She loves taking a raw piece of wood, cutting it with her skill saws, gluing or nailing it into the shape she desires, painting, and finishing it until the project is what she had in her mind's eye when she began. She gets her ideas from magazines, television shows (making me watch Christopher Lowell when I go to her house for coffee), even other craft fabricators.

Mona tells me this activity helps change her perspective on events in her life. Changing her perspective helps change her thoughts and, thus, her feelings of stress. The fact that she has something of beauty (remember, beauty is in the eye of the beholder) when she is finished is a by-product, not the reason for engaging in the activity.

▶ Twyla loves book stores, a passion she shares with her husband. We don't even have to purchase anything in order to have this activity bring us joy. A book store seems to renew our passion for reading and recharge our souls from the rigors of our daily lives. An hour in a book store is therapeutic for both of us, changing our perspective on events we are enduring together. Again, changing our perspective changes our thoughts and, in turn, changes our feelings of stress.

There are people who find shopping in general to be an activity they enjoy. I would encourage those who find this to be true to examine why they enjoy this. As you will see in the next example, the accumulation of possessions can be stressful, as it can increase your consumer debt, making your financial situation tighter, and adding to the negative aspects of your daily life.

▶ There is much being written today about simplifying your life in order to help with feelings of stress. This is not a new concept by any stretch of the imagination. Socrates observed a life unexamined is not a life worth living. The Quakers believed in the doctrine of simplification, as did the Puritans. Even the hippies of the 1960s wanted to live life more simply than their parents. Henry David Thoreau wrote the quintessential guide for simplification in *Walden* published in 1854. Thoreau said he went to the woods because "I wished to live deliberately, to front only the essential facts of life and see if I could not learn what it had to teach and now when I came to die, discovered I had not lived."

In a recent article regarding simplifying, the author stated that many in today's society are suffering from "affluenza"—a condition of "swollen expectations, feverish consumption, rising debt and constant fatigue." How wonderfully worded.

When we are constantly consuming, constantly shopping for new possessions, we become a slave to not only the idea of acquiring more, but to the debt associated with it. I wrote a chapter in a book titled *Possibilities II*, where I discussed the enslaving nature of consumer debt. If you are in debt today, one of the most important endeavors you may engage in is eliminating it. Simply put, you have overspent your income to acquire it, you must underspend in the future to pay it off. Not only will this allow you a great sense of accomplishment when you are debt free, it may eliminate the health problems created by stress.

A recent study done by Ohio State University and the University of Alabama reported the people with higher consumer debt in comparison to their income were in worse health in general.

A more simple lifestyle is one change you may want to make in your life in order to not only change your perspective but to change your health.

▶ A running buddy of mine, Stan Sweeney, loves to fly. He owns a single-engine plane and flies it every chance or excuse he can find. He flies to business meetings, his daughter's cross-country races, family vacations, and events. When given the opportunity, he takes it. Is it overcoming the gravitational pull of the earth that he enjoys, the attention to detail that is essential for a safe flight, or the thrill of doing something many consider dangerous? No matter what the reason, Stan flies and loves it. I'm sure the beneifits he receives outweigh the risk for him.

▶ My Grandmother Rader, besides being an accomplished painter, loved to sing. She sang in the church choir, for family holidays, or just while she was going about her daily chores around the house.

She said to me once, "I don't sing because I am happy, I am happy because I sing." What a wonderful testament for an activity helping reduce stress. When she sang, it changed her perspective on events in her life and, when she did that, her thinking naturally changed, as did her feelings.

Sing, play an instrument, or just listen to music you love. The benefits are tremendous.

▶ As mentioned earlier, Maggie and I are involved in the local community theater. When the group tries out for a new production, it is almost exclusively the same people. These individuals all have jobs and families, yet they are willing take on more activity and responsibility because they love the challenge of being in front of an audience. Though the anxiety of performing is evident minutes before going onstage, the activity helps those individuals with the stress in their daily lives.

Try acting, speaking, or any other activity where you must perform in front of an audience. You may find it actually has the opposite effect of what many think.

▶ As most people learn, close friends can be a wonderful outlet to helping you change your perspective on events. As you share your burdens with friends, they can offer comfort, advice, or just a nonjudgmental ear to listen to your concerns, fears, or thoughts. This is a natural way to change your perspective on events.

Friendship offers two ways to change your perspective on situations in your life. Not only can you share your situations with the friend, but as they share problems with you, you may find your perspective on your situations changes.

I spoke in Moberly, Missouri, a few weeks ago and it offered me the opportunity to stay with family friends. Gene and Darlene Bamman have been friends with my parents since they were in the Marine Corps fifty years ago. The Bammans lost both of their daughters to tragic illnesses, Cindy when she was six years old and Debbie when she was twenty-seven.

I was fortunate to have had a relationship with Debbie that began when I was a child. Though she was five years older than me, we had much in common. We loved sports, music and sharing a laugh. She was a close friend, confidante and mentor. I was even able to be at the hospital on the afternoon she died. She remains part of my life even today as I remember so many great times with her.

While staying with the Bammans, I had the opportunity to talk with them about Debbie. I was also able to see so many of the landmarks I remember while being with her. There was the road where she and I ran, the side yard where we drank milk shakes on hot, summer evenings, the school yard where I broke my leg playing football. Even the drive in where she took me to see a scary movie. She asked me a number of times during the show if I was scared. I told her I wasn't, but I could tell she knew I was lying. She was kind enough to not point this out to the others, as I was by far the youngest and it would have undoubtedly led to their teasing me. I slept in Debbie's bed that night, and the room brought back so many memories they are too numerous to list here.

The following day, with the words exchanged with my dear friends the night before still echoing in my head, I drove back in silence to the Kansas City airport. It was strange that even though my memories and the previous evening's conversation persistently brought tears to my eyes, I wanted to experience them, to cling to them, even to cherish them.

This experience allowed me to more alertly realize what Gene and Darlene go through daily. If only the twelve hours affected me that dramatically, how must those same sights affect them? The empathy experienced for my friends changed my perspective on problems in my life. How can I get angry at the children for not doing their chores when the Bammans don't have their children to get angry with?

Seeing a friend's situation can help you keep your own problems in perspective. Be a friend.

▶ Pets are a wonderful means for helping people change their perspective on situations. I already alluded to my cat, but we have all experienced the unconditional love of a pet. Research tells us pets help people live longer, healthier lives. Being loved by a pet may make the difference in your perspective on situations.

If you are looking for a pet, contact your local animal shelter, the humane society, or give me a call as I have two dogs, a cat, and a neighbor I wouldn't mind parting with.

▶ Other activities you might want to consider include cooking, reading, volunteering, fishing, collecting things like spoons, plates, etc., taking a nightly hot bath, going to the salon for your hair or nails, eating out, or going to the movies on occasion.

No matter what activity you engage in, make sure it is something you enjoy doing and something that is not destructive to your body, mind, family, or spirit.

Taking time to do things you enjoy does require time, but the benefits far outweigh the time given up doing something else. Right now, I want you to take a minute and schedule something you would like to do in the next week. Go ahead, put it on your calendar as you would an important business meeting or an activity done for the benefit of someone else. When someone asks you in the coming days to do something during that time period, you can honestly tell them you have an appointment at that time. You will not be lying to them as you will have an appointment for your own mental health.

Follow the same pattern weekly for the next four weeks as it will make it a natural part of your week. Though it takes time away from other activities, you will find you return to your family, career, and life more focused and better equipped to handle the stress associated with them because you have ***Let It Go, Just Let It Go!***

Let It Go—Just Let It Go!

Chapter 10

Mindfulness

Our past and our future simultaneously exist in our present.

—Taro Gold in *Open Your Mind, Open Your Life*

As was mentioned earlier, there have been few people in my life that I loved more, or even as much, as Twyla's mother, Emma Lou. She and I hit it off from the first moment we met. Probably because we shared a common love for Twyla and Keith in the beginning, we were allowed the opportunity to forge our own love for each other.

In the spring of 1997, after eighteen months, three surgeries, two rounds of chemotherapy and one round of radiation, we received the news that Emma Lou's cancer had returned. The physicians told us what we already suspected and that was there was really nothing they could do for her. Knowing we were entering our final days with this woman who meant so much to all of us was an unbearable emotional burden for me! I wanted to run from it, avoid it, and make the reality disappear. I'm ashamed to say that I tuned out mentally those final three and a half months.

I immersed myself in work, traveling whenever possible so I wouldn't have to witness her daily decline. I engaged in less productive activities than work as well. No matter what I did, I could not escape from the pain of knowing my time with this woman was limited.

So many of her final days I spent in a blur of anything but mindfulness of the moment. Though my time was limited with her, I allowed the pain of the inevitable future to keep me from enjoying those final days, an opportunity I will regret to my dying day.

Instead of spending every moment I could with her, soaking up time with her like bricks soak up the heat from a hot summer day, I tuned out. Even the time I spent with her physically, I was not always present mentally.

On August 15, 1997, as I awoke in a hotel room in Sulphur, Oklahoma, I received a call from Twyla that her mom was entering her final hours. Even then, I couldn't face the pain of reality. I got up, ran, showered, dressed, and went to work like the day would hold no more significant event than accounting. About 2:00 P.M. I drove the three hours home, arriving at Emma Lou's house.

I entered the bedroom of my in-laws' house and found Twyla's mom in bed. Her father was there, as well as Twyla. I am at least thankful that I was mindful during the next hour. I spoke with Emma Lou. Though she could no longer communicate with words, she expressed the same love for me as she had for the past few years. One of my comments even got her to laugh as best she could at that moment. About 6:00 P.M. she took her last breath, and as she exhaled she slipped peacefully into her eternal rest.

Yes, that moment pains me every time I think of it. Even today, I cry as I write these words, but that moment taught me an important lesson. Even in this, one of only five or six of the most painful moments of my entire life, I could survive even if I were present. The pain I was feeling wouldn't kill me. Losing someone you love is just a natural part of loving someone deeply. If I am going to love someone, I am going to one day have to part with him or her. The pain felt at this parting is in direct proportion to the love felt for that person. If I am going to love, I am one day going to feel the great pain of loss.

I believe Emma Lou hung on in those final hours in order to help teach me a valuable lesson of life. Knowing the physical pain she was enduring and the fatigue she felt from a long battle with a disease makes this one of the most unselfish gifts ever bestowed on me. She gave me a moment of mindful pain and in doing so, taught me about life and love. I will always love her and cherish my time with her. I will see you again, Emma Lou.

When we live mindfully, being present in the current moment without concern for the moments that have passed or the moments that have yet to pass, we find our stress level naturally diminishes. When you think of it, very few of our daily moments are filled with stressful events. Our stress usually is derived from thoughts about the future or the past. When we recognize that stressful feelings arise from our thoughts and we are the creator of these thoughts, we can gently bring our attention back to what we are doing and where we are at the current time.

WE PRACTICE MINDFULNESS BY REMEMBERING TO BE PRESENT IN ALL OUR WAKING MOMENTS.

—Jon Kabat-Zinn, Ph.D., from *Full Catastrophe Living*

This chapter has given me trouble. Though the rest of the book is done, this chapter continues to be the problem child of the book. This is my fourth attempt at writing it as the three previous attempts have yielded nothing to give Milli Brown, my publisher. It is my belief that the problem stems from the consternation of knowing, like so many people who have passed before me, that remaining mindful of the present, living in the present moment or whatever you would like to label it is one of the finest activities you can engage in for your own emotional health. The consternation comes from the fact that, though you may realize it is the way to live, it is so very difficult to remain mindful from moment to moment.

Traditional Buddhist texts speak of the "monkey mind," and this seems to be the most accurate description of what most of our minds are like from day to day. Monkey mind refers to one's mind jumping from thought to thought like a monkey would jump from one tree to the next without taking notice of the individual trees. Like the monkey, your mind cannot find what it is looking for unless it takes time to slow down and notice what is going on in the present moment. Remember the meditation practice we tried in the chapter on physical activity? Remember how you were able to remain focused on your breathing for maybe ten or twenty counts, then your mind wandered to your next appointment, what the kids have scheduled after school today, or the chapter of the book that is giving you so much trouble? Perhaps your thoughts were diverted to some hurt in the past, something your spouse said to you yesterday, or an incident from your childhood.

No matter what, your mind was quickly diverted from being focused on the counting of your breaths to something else. When we noticed our mind had wandered, we were to take notice of what took us to the next thought. Once we had done that, we were to gently, and without judgment, bring our focus back to our breathing. This is what is meant by monkey mind.

Our minds are constantly at work and jumping from one thought to the next. Remembering that our feelings are derived directly from our thoughts and knowing that our minds are constantly jumping from one thought to the next, you can begin to see why your feelings can change at the drop of the hat. When you are able to remain mindful of the present moment, you will rarely be consumed with stressful feelings because your mind will rarely be generating stressful thoughts. In fact, Richard Carlson states that feeling may be used to remind you to remain mindful. In *You Can Be Happy No Matter What,* he says:

> *Feelings are extremely helpful in detecting when our mind has stepped from the present moment. It's pretty likely, for*

example, that when we are feeling bothered, annoyed, or frustrated, that our thinking has somehow wandered from the present. The next time you're stressed or frustrated, take a quick, honest look at where your thoughts are. Almost certainly you'll be thinking about all you have to do in the future, or everything you did earlier in the day, or of something unpleasant that happened or may happen tomorrow. Rarely, when we are upset, will your thoughts be centered in the present. Most of the time, the present moment is quite peaceful.

When you are feeling stressed, obviously you must return to mindfulness of the present moment. As with our breathing, in meditation, when you notice feeling stressed about a situation, let it remind you to refocus your attention on the moment at hand. Also, as with the breathing meditation, take notice of the thought which led your mind away from the task at hand, then gently and without judgment bring your attention to the present.

It dawned on me this morning that the problem with this chapter for me was the fact that I too often take myself out of the present moment. I feel frustrated by my own monkey mind and having to write about it seems to be hypocritical. What got me off dead center was reading and understanding that more enlightened people including Lama Surya Das, Jesus Christ, Thich Nhat Hanh, and Sylvia Boorstein have struggled with this too!

I began experimenting with sitting meditation about twelve years ago and found it not to be for me. What I found was I didn't need to do sitting meditation to be mindful. There were opportunities for mindfulness every moment of my day. My morning pages, my running, my time with my family, my evening walk with Twyla and the dogs, my weight workouts, drinking a cup of coffee with my friend Mona, and even my speaking are all opportunities for mindfulness. So are the times I am doing the dishes, folding the laundry, picking up my messy office, or cleaning the downstairs bathroom. All of the items discussed in this book up to this point offer you the opportunity to be mindful of the present moment instead of obsessively thinking thoughts which are causing you stress. However, you can find mindfulness in anything you are engaged in during your day.

This morning, my monkey mind is jumping between the trees of compulsively worrying about some new material for a program I am going to deliver in Louisville, Kentucky, next Saturday and finishing this book. It dawns on me as I sit on flight 930 to Houston that if the plane goes down, neither of these will be problems any longer! Instead of letting my monkey mind take me away from a calm, relaxed mood, I will bring my mind back to the coffee I am drinking and the writing of these words. That way, if the flight goes down, my final moments won't have been spent in turmoil about things that never came to pass, but in the present with the coffee, pen, and paper. I would anticipate those last few seconds before we hit the ground would be a bit anxious because I was living mindfully, but at least I would be present! I wonder if I could get something stronger than coffee for the descent?

Today, I take the opportunities to bring my attention to what I am doing in a number of ways. I have found that speaking does cause anxiety from time to time. I had a speaker tell me early on that after doing the same material for a long period of time, I would become stale from it as it would become too routine for me. She said this can be death for a speaker because the quality of the performance will deteriorate. Her advice was to always be writing new material not only to off set this routineness, but to increase my level of anxiety because I never know how new material will go over with an audience. She told me to use this anxiety as my way of honoring my audience.

I incorporate this advice into my work by writing at least one new story to tell every month. I have found her advice has had its desired effect because I am always trying something new. I have found that my anxiety does go up, especially the first two or three times I tell the story. My anxiety is increased because I memorize all of my programs, and I worry I might leave out an important component of the story. I usually know that the concept is funny but have found that I must often change how it is originally worded in order to make it funny for the audience. One of my stories about being stopped by police with a drug dog at an airport simply required changing a word. Once I changed the word from "searched" to "stopped" it made the line one of the funniest of the story.

I have found that the best programs I perform are those that I am totally mindful about and not anxious of the new story coming up later. A few years ago, I read a paragraph from *Working Out, Working Within* by Jerry Lynch and Chungliang Al Huang. I have this paragraph copied in a special book I carry with me, and I read it about five to ten minutes before going on in front of an audience. It is as follows:

> *When talking to an audience, rather than obsess about your performance, get in touch with your essence, your purpose and your heart and simply deliver your message from an inner, more spiritual focus. You will gather your inner strength from focusing on the process and the moment-to-moment unfolding of events.*

When I read these lines, my body seems to instantly relax, my mind begins to focus on the topic at hand. My mind does not worry about mistakes made during the program because the moments of those mistakes are gone. Nor does the new story coming up thirty minutes from now cause concern because I am present with the story at this moment.

Doing this has helped me become a better performer on the speaking stage, but it also helps me become a better writer, a better father, a better husband, a better runner, better at domestic chores like dishes and laundry, and anything else I choose to engage in during my days here on earth.

As I am focused on the "moment-to-moment unfolding of events," I believe it offers me the greatest opportunity for spontaneous humor. For years now, I have found that at least one or two opportunities present themselves to be spontaneously funny in every program. Being blessed with a quick wit, I can give everyone in the room, including me, a quick laugh. It happens so routinely now that I look for them and greet them like long lost friends when they come. If my mind were put on automatic pilot while I tell a story for the seventy-fifth time, I would miss these opportunities.

Sylvia Boorstein, in her book *It's Easier Than You Think,* says the following:

> *Mindfulness is the aware, balanced acceptance of present experience. It isn't more complicated than that. It is opening to or receiving the present moment, pleasant or unpleasant, just as it is, without either clinging to it or rejecting it.*

How beautifully she puts things!

Sylvia further states the practice of mindfulness "deconditions the mind from its habitual pattern of running from discomfort." I have personally found this to be true. On the days in which my own mindfulness seems astute, not only is my emotional compass better, but the discomfort I experience doesn't seem unbearable. Twyla lecturing me about doing the laundry but not folding it, the children's constant need for money, even this chapter which has been such an annoyance don't seem to get to me. As I am mindful one day, I find it perpetuates mindfulness the following day. Unfortunately, not being mindful also perpetuates non-mindfulness as well.

The great hope of sitting meditation is to train the monkey mind how to stop jumping from thought to thought, but it is also intended for us to begin recognizing how the mind wanders from the moment at hand to some other thought. When we recognize this process, we can gently and without passing judgment bring our mind back to the present moment.

If you experiment with sitting meditation, you will want to bring that mindfulness to your other activities of the day. When you do the dishes next time, try doing them as the Vietnamese teacher Thich Nhat Hanh did his. He wrote in his book *The Miracle of Mindfulness*:

> *While washing the dishes, one should only be washing the dishes, which means that while washing the dishes, one should be completely aware of the fact that one is washing the dishes. At first glance, that might seem a little silly: why put so much stress on a simple task? But that's precisely the point. The fact that I am standing there and washing the bowl is a wondrous reality. I'm being completely myself, following my breath, conscious of my presence, and conscious of my thoughts and actions. There's no way I can be tossed around mindlessly like a bottle slapped here and there on the waves.*

He further says that if you can't be mindful while being engaged in an activity you dislike, or at least tolerate, then you probably will have difficulty being mindful when engaged in an activity you enjoy! Thich Nhat Hanh states the following:

> *If while washing dishes, we think only of the cup of tea that awaits us, thus hurrying to get the dishes out of the way as if they were a nuisance, then we are not "washing the dishes to wash the dishes". . . . If we can't wash the dishes the chances are we won't be able to drink our tea either. While drinking the cup of tea, we will only be thinking of other things, barely aware of the cup in our hands. Thus we are sucking away into the future—and we are incapable of actually living one minute of life.*

When I was training hard for marathons, it was necessary for me to do longs runs at least twice per week. My training plan called for a fifteen-mile run at about 6:00-per-mile pace on Thursday evening and a twenty-five to twenty-nine-mile run at about 7:00-per-mile pace on Sunday morning. These runs took three and a half hours and were physically as well as mentally grueling. As the length of these runs increased, I found my mind did well for up to three hours without much trouble, but the last thirty to forty-five minutes exacted a mental toll on me. I tried everything to mentally endure these last few minutes including imagining being in the final miles of my upcoming marathon, how I would handle the competition, visualizing the warm shower, cool drink and hot meal that awaited me upon completion of the run, even singing the theme song from sitcoms like "The Beverly Hillbillies," "Gilligan's Island," and my personal favorite, "Petticoat Junction."

One day when the final miles of a twenty-seven-mile run were taking their toll, I decided to focus on my body and how it felt in the moment. My right foot was landing a bit further back from my forefoot where it usually strikes the pavement, my arms were fatigued and were beginning to rise upward, and my left hamstring didn't feel as bad as usual.

With focusing on my body in the moment, the final miles passed with little problem. This was a great revelation for me, one that has carried me through many more long training runs.

Much to my delight, four years after making this discovery, while reading an article in a running magazine, I discovered the greatest runners in the world used much the same technique when they were competing and training! Focusing on the activity that was causing pain instead of tuning out seemed to make the effect of the pain less on the body and mind. This allows runners to endure more physically just by the way the pain was handled mentally. Since then, I have read this to be an effective way in dealing with chronic pain in patients in hospitals and physicians offices.

When presented with activities, both pleasant and unpleasant, focus on being mindful of the present moment, especially during stressful times. This will allow your thoughts to stay away from concern for the future or resentment of the past.

All the activities of this book—writing, humor, physical activity, compassion, family relationships and mindfulness—are intended to change your perspective on events in your life which are causing you thoughts of stress and thus stressful feelings. These will only work when you are mindful of the activity of the moment. As with meditation, when stressful thoughts arise, you can dismiss them by simply recognizing these thoughts, realizing they are simply your thoughts, generated within the depths of your own mind, and don't need to concern you any more than other thoughts. Remaining mindful of your thoughts will allow you to recognize this earlier and not allow stressful thoughts to run rampant.

One of the most important lessons you may learn is, when you open yourself up to the suffering and pain you have been trying to avoid, it does two things for you. First of all, you learn that you can survive this suffering. Second, you open yourself up to the lessons of life.

The Buddha was born into wealth and was shielded by his family from all human suffering, including the fact that all humans die. Only when he opened himself up to the suffering of the world by leaving the shelter of his kingdom did he find his own spiritual awakening. Jesus also opened himself up to the suffering of the cross for the greater good of mankind.

We have innumerable opportunities daily to practice mindfulness. Anytime you wake up to the present, whether it be washing dishes, exercising, tasting your meal tonight, talking with your children about their ball game or lessons from school, touching the skin of your lover, watching the sunset, reading these words, or even writing your thoughts, you have tuned into the present moment and awakened to mindfulness. As you wake to mindfulness of the here and now, your stress level will immediately decline.

As Lama Surya Das said in *Awakening the Buddha Within,*

"This is the starting point as well as the goal. Between these two—origin and goal, the ground and the fruit—lies the path. Fully inhabit this present moment. It's worth it." This will allow you to ***Let It Go, Just Let It Go!***

CHAPTER 11

Creative Problem Solving

The creation of something new is not accomplished by the intellect but by the play instinct acting from inner necessity.

—C. G. Jung

When Maggie was three years old, I transferred to a hospital in Lenexa, Kansas, to be the C.F.O. Have you ever taken a job and ten minutes into that job, you knew it was a mistake? Well, that was this job! I hated it for the entire ten months we were there! It was so bad, we called the hospital "The Pit of Despair" after the dungeon in *The Princess Bride.* Our children still call it that when we drive by it during trips back to Kansas City.

Twyla was still working on her degree when we moved there, and she decided to take a pottery class at the University of Kansas. This class met one morning per week, and I decided to take Maggie to work with me for an hour or two on these days.

Now those of you who have had a three-year-old child in your presence, you know they cannot read, but they can sure recognize those golden arches. One morning while we were driving to work, Maggie looked over at me and said, "Hey, Daddy, let's stop at McDonald's and get us an ice cream cone!"

Now when a father is presented with this type of situation, he has choices. He can do the wrong thing and stop and buy the ice cream cone, or he can do the right thing and explain to his daughter that she cannot have ice cream at 7:00 A.M. Well, at this time in my life, I was probably more inclined to do the wrong thing and just buy her the ice cream, but on this particular morning I was running late for work and had to do the right thing.

Like many fathers, though I had to do the right thing, I couldn't take that kind of hit with my children, especially with my daughter, so I did what 95 percent of fathers would do if presented with a similar situation. I looked at Maggie and said, "You know your momma won't let you have ice cream at seven o'clock in the morning!"

Well, it seemed to appease her, as she didn't say anything else for a few miles. All of a sudden she had an "ah-ha" idea! She looked at me and said, "Hey, Daddy, let's not tell her!" like she was the first person to think that you don't always have to tell the truth. I wanted to say, "Yes, then we will go visit an old girlfriend of mine and we won't tell her about that either," but I didn't.

Creativity

In the opening chapter, I said that the first step to reducing stress in our lives is to understand that our stress is not inherent to situations but is based upon our thoughts. I said that this was not a prescription to pretend that situations do not bother us, but to recognize that the stressful feelings are based upon our thoughts. Once you deal with changing your thoughts, you can begin to deal with the situations with creativity but only after you have changed your perspective and learned how to access your creativity.

When you use writing, humor, physical activity, or any of the other methods you may choose to change your perspective on the stressful events of your life, you are moving your mind into an arena where you can access our creativity for solving problems. As we do this, we must first understand how our minds come up with creative solutions to our problems.

Richard Carlson and Joseph Bailey wrote a book titled *Slowing Down to the Speed of Life,* and they outline two modes of thought we have at our disposal. First, there is the processing mode of thought. This is housed in the left hemisphere of our brain. We use our processing mode for memorizing information, analyzing data, planning our lives, and solving problems where all the variables of the equation are known, such as an algebraic equation. This allows us to learn tasks and then be able to repeat them easily. It is the mode of thought our schools are accustomed to teaching because they are usually teaching new skills in the traditional classroom setting. We are accustomed to using this in accounting and much of the business world because so many decisions today are determined by what the financial ramifications will be on the organization.

As you can see, there are situations where this is not only appropriate but beneficial because it best suits the situation. Consequently, there are situations where the processing mode of thought isn't the best. When a circumstance presents itself and not all of the variables are known, using the processing mode of thought can be a frustrating and stressful experience.

Currently, we are dealing with a situation with one of our children where not all of the variables are known. It involves a coach of Maggie's who doesn't communicate well with her. The coach has ignored Maggie and moved her to a position which is foreign to her, and he refuses to allow her to compete for the fielding positions she has played for the past seven years.

The problem with this situation is not the change in her position. It is the lack of communication on the part of the coach as to why she has changed positions. He has not told her why she is better suited for the new position, what she is doing wrong or not doing in her old positions, what skills she needs to improve on in order to get a shot at competing, nothing! He has just moved her, and Maggie's perception is her skills have somehow diminished.

Not only are we unaware of the reasons for moving her to a new position, we are not very familiar with this coach and don't know how he will respond if we address him. When others have addressed similar situations with him, he apparently doesn't communicate with them and they seem to be punished for questioning his judgment. Maggie is concerned he will respond in a defensive manner, which I am sorry to say seems to be too often the way when one questions a coach's decision. Will he be vindictive and bench her altogether so she doesn't get a chance to play? Will he try to intimidate her or us if we broach the subject?

We have tried to use our processing mode of thought to figure out an answer to this situation and have found it to be stressful and frustrating, and we still have come to no positive and beneficial solution! The main problem is we have been engaging the wrong side of our brain to solve the situation. We would be much better served using the other mode of thought rather than our processing mode in this situation.

The other mode of thought is known as the free-flowing mode. It is housed in the right hemisphere of the brain and, according to Richard Carlson and Joseph Bailey, operates much like a river, always flowing with new information and thoughts. Some of these thoughts and information come from our memory, where our brain remembers similar situations and the solution to those problems. Some of the ideas come from the well of creativity which all of us possess. The main problem is that most of us do not know how to access it because, in our modern, rushed and too often complicated society, we have been taught to rely on the processing mode of thought for all situations.

The free-flowing mode of thought is not accustomed to rational thinking and the primary purpose is to help us perform at our optimal level. It is what Keith Richards of the Rolling Stones uses when he writes a new song. It is what Twyla uses when she creates a new pot on the wheel. Edgar Degas tapped into his free-flowing mode of thought when he painted *The Dancing Class, Dancers on Stage 'L' Etoil,* or any of his other paintings. Though too many coaches are ignorant to the fact, it is the mode of thought accessed when an athlete is performing well.

Michael Jordan, arguably the greatest athlete of our generation, has learned to access, on a regular basis, his free-flowing mode of thought when he plays basketball. Though he possesses many superior physical skills, it is thought his greatness comes not from these, but from his mental toughness on the court.

Phil Jackson, in his book *Sacred Hoops: Lessons of a Hardwood Warrior,* believes Michael Jordan has attained the quality of mind that few athletes, as well as few Zen masters, have been able to achieve. Coach Jackson said Michael's "ability to stay relaxed and intensely focused in the midst of chaos is unsurpassed. He loves being in the center of a storm. While everyone else is spinning madly out of control, he moves effortlessly across the floor, enveloped by a great stillness."

Jackson stated that Michael, when presented with a situation that most athletes believe to be filled with pressure and stress, will call upon the memory of a similar situation in his past where he has been successful.

Rather than cloud his mind with negative thoughts, he says to himself, "Okay, I've been here before," then tries to relax enough to let something positive emerge. Jordan doesn't believe in trying to visualize the shot in specific detail. "I know what I want the outcome to be," he says, "but I don't try to see myself doing it beforehand."

When you enlist your free-flowing mode of thought, your thinking is effortless, creative, and fully present in the current moment. Thoughts are stress free, non-fatiguing, enjoyable, and allow for optimal performance.

Richard Carlson and Joseph Bailey say we have complete access to these two modes of thought at all times, but we must learn how to access them. If you are wanting to access your processing mode of thought, or the left hemisphere of your brain, you simply focus you attention on the problem. If you are helping your fourteen-year-old daughter with her algebra, you must focus your attention on the problem, not on trying to watch "That '70s Show" while you do it. (Take it from someone who knows!)

If you want to access your free-flowing mode of thought, you must do two things. You must stop focusing your attention on the problem, and you must relax. Richard Carlson refers to a survey about where people get their best ideas, and the top three places were as follow:

- The shower
- While on vacation
- Driving to and from work

What do these three places have in common? First of all, you are probably not focusing your attention on the problem at hand, and second, you are probably relaxed.

When you access your creativity, you will get one of those "ah-ha" type of ideas! In order to do this, you must stop focusing your attention on the problem and you must relax. Richard Carlson and Joseph Bailey equate accessing these modes to using a walkie-talkie. You are either on talk or listen and there isn't any in between. To talk, you press the button in; to listen, you let out on the button. To access your processing mode of thought, you concentrate on the situation, just as pressing the talk button. To access your free-flowing mode of thought, you stop focusing your attention on the problem, or let out on the talk button. This allows your mind to relax and flow from one thought to the next without interference. I watched this happen firsthand a number of years ago with my daughter.

Maggie entered into her free-flowing mode of thought when she came up with the idea to not tell her mom about the ice cream from MacDonald's that morning. She wasn't focusing on the problem, and she was relaxed when she came up with a solution to a problem that was causing her anxiety.

As you change your perspective on events by doing some of the activities mentioned earlier, you not only stop focusing on your problems, you will also begin to relax. This helps you access your creativity so that you may come up with quality solutions to these problems.

Returning to our situation with Maggie's coach. When it occurred to me my mind was using the wrong side of my brain to develop a quality solution to this problem, I began using my writing to help me change my perspective on the situation. These writings have taken the form of both my morning pages and longhand spasms to release much of the stress I have been feeling about this situation and the coach himself. I have written in the neighborhood of thirty pages of angry, hostile, even vile thoughts about him, his ignorance about dealing with people, his lack of sensitivity to the situation, even possible ulterior motives he may have for doing this particular injustice.

I have written during some of Maggie's games, on flights during the past two weeks, in hotel rooms early in the morning over a steaming cup of coffee, even while driving my car on the Oklahoma turnpike. The latter afforded me the opportunity to get to know one of our state's newest troopers stationed in Rogers County, Oklahoma. Apparently while I was pouring out my anger about this situation onto the pages of a longhand spasm, some of it spilled over onto my gas pedal, accelerating my care from the posted speed limit of seventy-five to an evidently unacceptable eighty-seven miles per hour.

These writings have allowed me to change my perspective from the future harm that might come from these activities back to the present moment. Returning to mindfulness of the present moment has allowed me to remember she is only a freshman in high school and will be moving, following this fall season, from the junior high team to the high school team and a different coach. The high school coach is a man whom I respect, one who I believe communicates his reasons for making changes to her fielding position. I realize she is playing and, though not at her usual position, the experience, if acquired in an accepting manner, will make her a better ballplayer. Maggie will also learn a life lesson that there are times when people less astute than she will have authority over her, and she must learn that these situations, though unfair, happen to everyone from time to time. The key is to not let it get you down while you endure it, and develop a plan to overcome it. Maintaining your self-esteem is especially important in this situation.

It has also allowed me to better come to grips with my feelings about deplorable coaches from my own athletic career. I believe this situation is especially difficult for me because of these past memories of coaches, due to ignorance or maliciousness, or a reprehensible combination of the two, who offered the potential to damage my athletic performance, instead of encouraging and mentoring me to improve. Instead, I've learned to become self-sufficient in my own training and suspect of anyone who goes by the title "coach."

With these realizations, I began to feel my emotional and physical posture start to relax, and I let my perceptions of the situation go! With that has come a calm that will allow me to be in the same state with this man but no longer wanting to intimidate or pound him! The stressful feelings and frustration have also subsided. To boot, my free-flowing mode of thought has sent me a steady stream of alternatives to this situation. Some are good and offer both the opportunity for Maggie to get an answer to her questions and to keep the relationship viable for the future. Some are not so good and would require me to possibly enter counseling, the Mangum City Jail or, in some cases, both.

Regardless of the final outcome, it is my belief that writing has allowed me to understand that the stress I am experiencing is coming from my own thoughts and helps me return to a mindfulness of the situation as it exists at the present moment. These realizations have allowed me to relax and stop focusing so much attention on the situation. That, in turn, has allowed me to develop a whole array of alternative solutions to the problem. These alternatives are, in most cases, all better than anything I came up with while trapped in the processing mode of thought.

This wisdom has been known for thousands of years. The *Tao Te Ching,* written 2500 years ago by Lao-tzu (551–479 B.C.) wrote about allowing your mind to become still and allowing the answer to rise from within you. He wrote, "Do you have the patience to wait till your mud settles and the water is clear? Can you remain unmoving till the right action arises by itself?" Further, Lao-tzu wrote, "Stop thinking and end your problems."

Both of these say to me that Lao-tzu knew about the free-flowing mode of thought and the powerful creative problem-solving skills contained within it long before modern psychology began to discover about hemispheres of the brain. When my mind has difficulty "letting go" of the processing mode of thought, the words of Lao-tzu help return my mind to the free-flowing mode of thought.

The book *Slowing Down To the Speed of Life* further points out that an essential key to accessing the free-flowing mode of thought is accepting the fact that you don't have a solution to the problem. Further, besides not having a solution to the problem, it is all right not to know what to do to solve the problem. The capacity to be humble enough to admit this will begin to open the door to the free-flowing mode of thought.

Dr. Carlson and Dr. Bailey state the following:

> *Our ego doesn't like not knowing and would prefer to go over and over what we already think and believe rather than trust in a subtle, unknown process like creative intelligence. But opening ourselves to the unknown is a peaceful, productive alternative to our business-as-usual processing mode where we pretend (or hope) that we know what's going on. By clearing the mind and admitting to ourselves that we don't know, we receive answers that are often brilliant, unexpected, and just right for the situation.*

Admitting not knowing is difficult for all of us because it points out to us that we aren't perfect, that we are ignorant in some arena, and that we don't have all of the answers. It does slap our ego, insults our self-esteem, even belittles our sensibilities. The discomfort felt during these times can often lead us to close our minds to new ideas and ways of doing things. That discomfort can return us to old ways and old thinking, the worst possible solution to situations where creativity is called for. Instead of looking to free-flowing thought, the ego tries to use the processing mode of thought in order to muscle its way through the situation.

When our minds open up to not knowing, resigning to our ignorance, we tap into our free-flowing mode of thought, and our stream of creative solutions begins to enter our consciousness until the most appropriate one presents itself. Some believe this is actually divine intervention. I heard Richard Pryor once say he was too often tired to always have the answers to his life, but he did much better emotionally and mentally when he "let go and let God." Wherever the answer comes from, admitting you don't know is an integral component to tapping into the universe's wisdom.

One of my favorite stories about being willing to be open and accepting of not knowing is about the classic Zen master who was asked to teach a pompous professor about Zen Buddhism. When the pompous professor entered the quarters of the Zen master, it was apparent to the master that the professor believed he knew all the answers to life's questions. After a couple of lessons, the master asked the professor if he would share some tea with him. The professor willingly accepted the offer for tea.

The Zen master brewed the tea and set the table with two small oriental tea cups. Being the quintessential host, the Zen master poured his guest's tea first. As the tea cup fills to the rim, the old master continues to pour tea. With tea overflowing onto the table, the pompous professor asks the master what he is doing. The master states, "When the cup is full of tea, I cannot pour any more into it. It is the same with your knowledge. In your opinion, your knowledge is already spilling over. How can I offer you any more?"

For just a moment, think of your greatest accomplishments. How many of these would you have accomplished if you had not been open to learning new ways of doing things? How many of these would be in your memory today if you had a closed mind to the wisdom of others or the universe?

It is my wish that this book has not only helped you understand where your stressful feelings come from, but also how you might redirect your thoughts away from stressful thoughts back to your mindfulness of the present moment.

Remember you are the architect of your stress. When you are presented with a situation, you instantly have thoughts about that situation. Those thoughts are your attempt to interpret that situation. Based upon that interpretation, you will have an emotional response or feeling. Also, remember your mood can bias your thoughts and, thus, your feelings. Regardless of what you do to change your perspective, you will want to return to your mindfulness of the moment because with this mindfulness, you will naturally begin to tap into your creative problem solving skills.

I close all of my speaking engagements with a quote from Sylvia Boorstein's book *It's Easier Than You Think*. Ms. Boorstein says:

Every single act we do has the potential of causing pain, and every single thing we do has consequences that echo way beyond what we can imagine. It doesn't mean we shouldn't act. It means we should act carefully. Everything matters.

I quote this not so much to share the wonderful insight of this woman with my audience, but more to remind myself of the importance of remaining mindful of my actions on a daily basis. When my actions cause pain, that pain does not just stop with the person I have interacted with. They will carry that pain into interactions with others, and there is the potential of the second person being harmed. We must act carefully with those we come into contact with on a daily basis. It is my hope that this mindfulness will in some small way help to make this a better world in which we all must inhabit.

May your days be filled with joy and may your life be filled with love and laughter. Remember to take care of yourself and ***Let It Go, Just Let It Go!***

APPENDIX A

Structured Physical Activity

We are born with a 70-year warranty, but many people never bother to read the instructions. Three score and ten, the Bible promises us. The instructions when we left Eden were simple enough: a six day work week and work that would bring sweat to our brow. The sweat of our brow, no longer necessary to earn our daily bread, has become even more necessary to make us fully functioning men and women. It now determines whether or not we will live a full 70-years and live those years at our full physical potential.

—George Sheehan, author and lifelong runner

If there is one area of my life where the forces of the universe have taught me a lesson, it is in regard to physical activity. Let me give you a brief history.

At a young age, I discovered I loved to run distances. During the third grade, my parents decided we should move from a house on North Institute Street in Richmond, Missouri, to a house on North Thornton, a distance of about a mile. Not only were we leaving the only house I had ever known, but the willow tree in the backyard where I spent countless hours playing cowboy! To boot, all of my friends were there. This was a devastating situation in my life.

The kids in the new neighborhood weren't into adventures on the open range. They were more into organized sports, including football, baseball, and hockey. Sports had never been big on North Institute Street, other than games like hide the belt and red rover, so I didn't fit in immediately with the other kids of the new neighborhood. We might as well have moved to Nepal! (Though at that time of my life I didn't know there was such a place as Nepal!)

The only positive aspect of this move was that, for the first time in my life, I was offered the opportunity to ride the school bus to and from school. Billy Joe Hardwick was the driver of bus number 55. On the first day, my soul was filled with excitement and anxiety for this new adventure. I boarded the bus, surveyed the setting and decided to sit down next to a very attractive, older girl whose last name was Ottursky. (She was much older than I as she was at least in junior high school.) The enjoyment of riding the bus lasted about a week before I grew bored with the length of time it took to get home! One day I decided not to ride the bus and walk home. I found that I could walk home in about the same time as it took to ride the bus. This was a more appealing situation than riding the bus because at least I was active in getting home.

Being a competitive Irishman, even at the age of ten, I decided that I would try to beat the bus home on a daily basis. During my walks home, I began to run intermittently. I quickly discovered that not only did the running become easier, I really enjoyed the activity. By the end of the school year, I was running the entire length of about a mile and a half home and loving every minute. (This is how all the great Kenyan runners begin their careers, though they do it at altitudes higher than that of Richmond, Missouri!)

This activity continued unaltered for the next three years. Every day my father would drop me at school on his way to work, then I would head home after school, running the whole way.

In September 1972, my running career was to get a vision! I watched two events that changed my life! The first was watching Frank Shorter win the Olympic gold medal in the marathon. He took the lead at fifteen kilometers and ran unchallenged the remainder of the way. He ran effortlessly, gliding along the street of Munich, Germany. Watching him enter the stadium and take his final lap on the Olympic track was the most thrilling event witnessed in my thirteen years! (There was an imposter who entered the stadium ahead of Shorter, but it didn't take any of the joy away from the event for me.)

The second event was watching Steve Prefontaine take fourth in the 5000-meter race. As Pre took the lead with a mile to go, my eyes were glued to the television! He ran a

4:02 final mile after completing over two miles before that! Unfortunately for Pre, Lasse Viren ran the final mile in 4:00. Pre's valiant efforts to pass Viren and Mohamed Gamoudi of Tunisia during the last lap were encouraged by my shouts from our family room in Richmond! In the home stretch, Pre was spent, staggering the final dozen meters as he was passed for the bronze medal by Ian Stewart of Great Britain. As I shed tears with Prefontaine, it was understood that I had just witnessed one of the most courageous races ever run! Following these two events, I knew I wanted to run for the remainder of my life.

As my junior high and high school years passed, though I tried my hand at football, basketball, and even wrestling, I never lost my love for running. Every spring I would read a book about Jim Ryan, the great Kansas University miler, and head for the track meets of Richmond High School! I even ran cross country during my senior year, though Richmond didn't offer it as a sport. I trained with the Excelsior Springs, Missouri, cross country team and traveled to meets either with them or alone.

I improved and continued to run for the track and cross country teams at William Jewell College at Liberty, Missouri. After college, I continued to train and improve, reaching personal best times of 30:50 for ten kilometers, 1:08:20 for a half-marathon (a race in which I was about thirty seconds ahead of Joan Benoit Samuelson, a feat I was very proud of since she won the first women's Olympic marathon about nine months later!) and 2:23:28 for the marathon!

About the age of thirty, my body began to rebel against the training that I had been putting it through for at least ten years. Up till that point, my training consisted of 105-mile weeks of running with two runs per day, except on Sunday, when I ran just one long run. My long runs sometimes reached twenty-nine miles in length! As my thirty-year-old body began to rebel against this stress, I continued to try to will it to accept the same workloads endured during my twenties.

In the past ten years, I have begun to redefine how I train this body! Gone is the arrogance of my youth when I looked at forty-year-old men and loved beating them because I just trained harder than they had! I have moved from training to be fast to training to be fit and healthy. I still love running and even love running fast, but those days are fewer in my training and spaced further apart! What follows are the lessons I have learned through thirty-five years of training.

The first thing you should do before beginning a structured exercise program is to consult with a physician who is physically active. (*Time* magazine had a survey reporting 68 percent of the physicians stated they had not exercised in the past year.) It is important that you consult with a physician who understands the elements of physical activity and, unfortunately, much of this knowledge must be learned through experience, not from one of those thick medical books.

For physical wellness, experts say exercise three times per week, twenty–thirty minutes per session. For emotional wellness, it is recommended five to six times per week. There are three areas that one must include in a structured exercise program.These are as follow:

- Aerobic or endurance training
- Strength or resistance training
- Flexibility or stretching exercises

Before we get too far into the discussion of a routine of exercise, we must explore a few concepts regarding training.

- **Hard/Easy Principle:** One of the most important aspects of training, one you will want to incorporate into your program immediately, is called the "Hard / Easy Principle."

  One of the most significant findings during the last fifty years with regard to training is that your body needs time for the effects of training to take place. If you work your body to the maximum daily, it will eventually not only break down via injury or illness, but by diminished performance as well. One of the mistakes by first time aerobic participants is they want to improve daily! This is simply not possible. Your body will react positively to the new stress (physical stress, not emotional stress, an important difference!) only if it has time to recover.

When you work your muscles through repetitive exercise, they will begin to adapt. A muscle that is worked will become more efficient and more comfortable performing the task. Given time, the body will supply more blood flow and energy to the muscle as your body begins the workout.

This transformation only takes place, though, if your body is allowed time to adapt to the current level of training and if the body is allowed adequate rest following workouts that stress the body's endurance. This is where the hard / easy principle comes in.

As you develop your weekly exercise routine, you must allow for days where you are going to stress your body (hard days) and days where you are going to allow your body to recover from these stressful workouts (easy days). My own routine for running indicates my body has a natural rhythm for the week. Tuesdays and Saturdays are the only days of the week that my workouts stress the body fully by running longer runs and of higher intensity. In fact, half of my week's mileage comes in these two days. Thursdays are moderate days, both in terms of mileage and intensity, and Wednesdays, Fridays, and Sundays are easy, running slowly and for shorter durations of time. My Monday workouts involve no running; instead, I use the Nordic Track or just walk, depending on how my body feels following the previous week's training. I don't know if the rhythm of my body is just a natural rhythm or if it is the result of thirty years of conditioning by training with this type of schedule. I do know it is a very ingrained in my schedule and life. (This is why I like speaking on Monday, Wednesday, and Friday as these do not interfere with my harder training days!)

Plan your week's workouts to include rest. If you want Tuesdays and Saturdays to be your aerobically challenging days, plan the five remaining days for easy workouts or no workout at all. When you incorporate strength training, you may want to have these workouts to be your easy or off-days of your aerobic training work. The most important concept for an organized workout program may be to follow the principle of hard/easy days.

▶ **Annual Restoration Period:** Along the principle of hard/easy workouts, your workout regimen should also include times of the year when the intensity and duration of your workouts are decreased for a mandatory rest period! Our bodies have a wonderful rhythm to them for not only a period of time as short as a week, but for times of year. When you begin to get more in touch with your body, you will find there are periods of the year when your exercise routine stagnates or becomes a burden. That is all right, and one of the most intelligent things you can do for your body is to honor this rhythm!

Again, with my own training, this is a lesson learned the hard way! (It is bad enough to have to learn the lesson the hard way, but in my case, I often have to have the lesson presented a number of times before I learn it! This is one of those lessons!) My time for extensive, harder training is the fall and winter leading up to the races that take place during the spring. My natural time for recuperation is the summertime. My body has no difficulty with cold temperatures but is greatly taxed during the hot summer months, especially in the heat of southwest Oklahoma. Temperatures here routinely exceed 100 degrees and reach as high as 120 degrees!

When you don't offer your body periods of rest from your normal routine, you will find your body experiencing a condition known in the running world as "overtraining." This is when your body loses its ability to recover from your more strenuous workouts, you feel fatigued most of the time, and your performances of both aerobic and strength workouts diminish. You are doing your body and mind no favor by continuing to train through this condition. The best advice when feeling this way is to back off your training program or completely disband it for a couple of weeks and take a month or two before resuming your normal routines.

Upon moving to Oklahoma nine years ago, I discovered this normal rhythm of my body over the year through experimentation. As my training throughout the long, hot summer rarely decreased from the winter levels, I would find myself feeling listless and fatigued by the first of September. When racing, my performances would suffer greatly during the fall races, even after the heat of the summer had subsided to the more moderate temperatures of our beautiful falls! About four years ago, I researched how my body would feel if my training was reduced for much of the summer! Much to my surprise, I discovered my performances in the fall were better following easier summer training than when my training during the hot summer was at the same level as the winter months. Now my regular routine is reducing my mileage and intensity of training for the long hot summer, running a race on Labor Day weekend to gauge my current level of fitness and building up for the months of September and October before resuming my more stringent training for November through April! Honoring my body's natural annual rhythms has afforded me a higher level of fitness during the majority of the year.

As you plan your year and plan your workout regimen, experiment with your body's natural annual rhythms and reduce your training for a three to four month period that coincides with your natural restoration time. Honoring your body is a wonderful, inexpensive present you can present to yourself annually!

▶ Develop an "I Am An Athlete" Attitude: As you build a physical training program, if you consider yourself an athlete in training, no matter what your previous thoughts were about athletes, you will find yourself more motivated.

My own experience has been that training is more important to me than competing! This will come as quite a surprise to my wife and children who know me as one of the most competitive individuals they have ever encountered. It is true, competition has always been a source of pleasure in my life, but I find a much larger void when I am unable to train due to injury or illness than when I have not competed for a period of time. In fact, much of my competition today is limited to running a local five-kilometer course every four weeks to note improvement in my time. Because of living in a rural area, I don't have much opportunity to have races close to home. With my extensive travel schedule for my speaking, having to be away from home for an additional day to race in Oklahoma City, Tulsa, or Dallas is not appealing to me. This hard effort every four weeks seems to fill the competitive void.

People ask me, "Kent, how can I be an athlete in training when I have been inactive for years and am carrying forty extra pounds?" Well, Webster's defines an athlete as "one who is trained or skilled in exercises, sports, or games requiring physical strength, agility or stamina." We have allowed our culture to define athletes as those guys we watch on "Sports Center" every morning performing superhuman feats of hitting a 96-mile-per-hour fastball over the left field wall, slam-dunking a basketball or scoring a hat trick on a top shelf slap shot! When you "train" your body for "physical strength, agility or stamina," you are an athlete, no matter how you compare with the next person!

In fact, research in the arena of endurance sports would indicate the person who simply completes an event, like a marathon or the Ironman Triathalon, at a slow time actually works harder than the winner. Because time spent exercising is longer for the jogger to complete the event than for the winner, the jogger must be trained to do this duration. Ask any world-class marathoner to run for five hours straight and they will look at you like you are kidding! Even when my training included twenty-nine-mile runs, they rarely lasted longer than three and a half hours and wasted me for the remainder of my Sunday!

We are all athletes, regardless of our current level of fitness or performance. As you begin your training, think of yourself as an athlete and your workouts will take on the flavor of those of world-class status.

▶ My running career has spanned a quarter of a century now, so my memory of the very beginning of it is foggy at best. What I have discovered through changes in my training routine, whether it be the addition of a new activity or the augmentation of an existing activity, is that it takes it four to six weeks before it is comfortable and integrated.

When investigating the reason for this, it seems our bodies begin to adapt to new physical activity in the first four to six weeks. If your activity is begun at a level where you are pushed gently, you will find in four to six weeks, this activity is now easier for you. You are ready for more advanced training. It isn't as difficult for you to accomplish what was at first difficult. This helps you grow in confidence toward physical activity and encourages you not only to continue with the activity but to grow in the activity.

The other reason for this is you will begin to notice the positive feelings associated with your newfound physical activity program. These positive feelings cause you to want to re-create them. If something feels good, you will naturally be motivated to re-create them, and this motivation comes from within yourself instead of from outside you. This is the natural high you get when you are working out, or what the University of Chicago research technician Mihaly Csikszentmihalyi, Ph.D., calls "flow."

In his book *Flow: The Psychology of Optimal Experience*, Dr. Csikszentmihalyi describes the "flow experience" as follows:

When the information that keeps coming into awareness is congruent with goals, psychic energy flows effortlessly. There is no need to worry, no reason to question one's adequacy. But whenever one does stop to think about oneself, the evidence is encouraging: "You are doing all right." The positive feedback strengthens the self, and more attention is freed to deal with the outer and inner environment.

When you reach this point, the physical activity you are engaged in becomes a habit for your life and you will continue, unlike the times in the past when you have tried physical activity and failed. If you commit to four to six weeks of activity and are doing something you enjoy, then you will make it a habit. Your internal motivation will continue to keep you involved in the activity.

▶ Goal Setting: One aspect people have found to be of benefit to maintaining their physical exercise program is setting and achieving a goal. Be careful with this one, as it can also be the same element that derails physical exercise programs! If your goals are too lofty, you may become discouraged and quit your program.

The book *Working Out, Working Within, The Tao of Inner Fitness Through Sports and Exercise* by Jerry Lynch and Chungliang Al Huang has one of the best descriptions of using goals for your exercise program. They describe goals as "lanterns illuminating the way" for your spirit to grow into a wellness program. They state that goals are "beacons that help to keep your soul on track and gain access into your deep passion. They are an integral component of an internal spirit quest, one that searches for and nurtures self-confidence and well-being. Goals help you to create a strong bond between what you dream and what you do." They continued,

In sports and exercise, once you begin to make this shift in consciousness, you open yourself up to opportunities to massage the spirit; you reduce unnecessary pressure and anxiety over trying to achieve the outcome or goal; you also cease to measure your self-worth based on the outcome and, therefore, nurture your self-esteem. The key is to set your goals in the spirit of passion, goals that are aligned with what you love, then proceed to enjoy thoroughly the process of following the direction they take you.

A good friend of mine, Dennis Stewart, is the epitome of using physical activity as a spiritual practice. During my high school years, he was my mentor for running. His instruction and advice, though not always heeded, were instrumental in my growth as an athlete. The really neat thing about Dennis is he continues to inform, inspire, and mentor me as my body ages and my training changes.

Dennis' attitude toward running and fitness was always more healthy than mine. While my training was too focused on competition, Dennis trained because he loved the physical activity. He listened to his body better and offered it times of recuperation while he engaged in physical activities other than running.

Following thirty years of teaching, Dennis retired in June 2000 "to focus on a wealth of outdoor adventures." He wants to canoe the entire length of the Missouri River, bicycle across the country, and continue to climb the highest point in all fifty states! In a letter to us he described one such activity which illustrates the goal-setting principle outlined above. Dennis scheduled a climb of Mount McKinley in June 2000, so he wanted to be prepared for it. He said, "We hiked the streets of Higginsville, Missouri, every night, as I increased my training routine for Mount McKinley, under the watchful eye of the local police. More than once they stopped us to find out why we were dragging large logs attached to our 50-pound backpacks through town."

Though he runs only three miles at a time, two to three times per week, he continues to have goals which help him develop his spirit through his passion for physical adventure. This has helped me develop goals for my own training outside of competition in order to renew my own spirit through my training. Thank you, Dennis, for your advice, honesty and love through these past twenty-five years.

Now, let's get into the three phases of a well-developed physical training program.

Aerobic Training

Aerobic or endurance training increases one's heart rate, creates a demand for oxygen, and involves the large muscle groups. Included here are walking, cross-country skiing, swimming, running, bicycling, and tennis. It is recommended that a physical exercise program include three to four sessions, twenty–thirty minutes per session, per week of uninterrupted aerobic training. Some hints for your aerobic workouts are as follow:

▶ Find what activities you enjoy! My activity is running, but I also love walking and cross-country skiing (though my opportunity to ski in southwest Oklahoma is limited to the Nordic Track machine I purchased a few years ago). My experiences swimming and bicycling have been disastrous, painful and life-threatening even.

About ten years ago, I experimented with swimming once a week. Being kind of competitive, I decided to work up to swimming a mile. A friend of mine, Bob McElligott, was routinely swimming a mile, and based upon that, it couldn't be that difficult. My weekly swims at the Southern Illinois University-Carbondale pool included adding a few laps per night!

In a few months, my body and mind were prepared to attempt the mile swim. Everything was going fine until about lap sixty when a cramp hit the arch of my left foot! The pain was excruciating! Massaging it was called for, but this offered a challenge as I was in the deep end of the pool when this cramp decided to strike! While massaging my foot, I would sink to the bottom. In order to survive, the massaging would have to cease and I would need to swim to the top to gain much needed air. The next few minutes were filled with massaging the foot while sinking to the bottom and swimming to the top for air while the cramp worsened.

The cramp finally loosened its grip on my arch, but it must have been quite a scene to see me floundering in the water like a dying whale! My respect for Bob heightened during that struggle, and my attempt to swim a mile was never again undertaken.

▶ Start slowly! If you have been inactive, a five-minute walk may be difficult for you, but you should exercise for the time frame that is comfortable. As you build up endurance, the same time frame will become easier for you to engage in. At that time, you can increase the workload gradually. One of the biggest mistakes people make in beginning a formal exercise program is they do too much too early! Their muscles get sore and they take a day off to let themselves recover. The first day off leads to two, then three, and they find themselves back in the sedentary lifestyle they were trying to escape by beginning this program.

▶ Some find exercising with others is a great motivator to begin and keep a program going. If you are one of these people, find someone who would like to begin the activity, and, throughout your program, remain working out with people at your current level of fitness.

▶ Channel any competitive instincts you may experience into seeing improvement in yourself, not competing against others! Competition is a dangerous emotion to experience in a physical training program, as it can lead you to do more than you are ready for at the current time (as witnessed by my swimming experience mentioned earlier).

Many cite this as a reason for not engaging in an organized exercise program. For many, the only acquaintance they have with exercise was the physical education classes they took in high school. These classes are too often associated with feelings of inadequacy because of the comparison to others inherent to them. When someone else is more physically gifted in the arena of sports, it makes you shy away from placing yourself in that arena again. (Thank goodness the physical education teachers of today are moving away from this type of class, but it is coming too slowly!)

When you feel the pangs of comparison or competition welling up inside you with regard to your physical exercise program, remember there is only one person you need to compare yourself with and that is you! Being the best you can be is the competitive outlet for your physical exercise program.

▶ Keep a log of your aerobic workouts in order to track your progress. This is a motivator that too few use in their exercise program. As you document and track your progress, this progress will inspire and motivate you to continue with your program.

▶ Use of a heart-rate monitor: A few years ago I decided to use a heart-rate monitor during my own training. I have never been known as one who worked too hard on my easy days (see Hard/Easy Principle above), but find it to be a good way to monitor the intensity of my harder workouts in order to make sure they are not too hard! Thus, my use of the monitor is limited to the two or three hard workouts per week which are intended to tax my running. On the easy days, my running is gauged by how my legs feel, and whenever in doubt, I slow down!

When performing aerobic exercise, your intensity can be gauged by the heart-rate zone you are working in. These zones are different based on the type of aerobic exercise you are engaged in. If you are running, you are having to support your entire weight with each step, thus your heart will need to work harder than if you are swimming, where your weight is supported by the water or bicycling, where your weight is supported by the frame of the bike.

As you choose an aerobic exercise and use a heart-rate monitor to gauge intensity of the workout, investigate the appropriate zones (expressed by percentage of maximum heart rate for the individual for that activity) for your current level of fitness and the activity. When your workouts call for an easier day, it has been my experience to make sure you are working too easy rather than too hard. Having workouts that are too intense for your fitness level can also lead to the dreaded state of "overtrained." (A heart-rate monitor is also a wonderful tool for diagnosing when one is "overtrained," as your resting heart rate will be higher and your lower intensity workouts will result in higher heart rates during exercise.)

Strength Training

Strength training is one of the most neglected components of exercise for most individual exercise programs. Strength or resistance training should be done two to three times per week in conjunction with your aerobic training. This is the component which was difficult for me to implement into my program, but one with major benefits as our bodies age.

As we reach our thirties, our muscle cells begin to revert to fat. A pound of fat burns fewer calories at a sedentary level than a pound of muscle. As this process continues, our sedentary metabolism continues to drop, meaning we burn fewer calories while watching TV than we did when we were twenty years old. This is why we can eat a whole package of Oreo cookies and drink a six-pack of beer during our college years without gaining an ounce. That same behavior at the age of thirty-five will cause us to balloon up to look like Louis Anderson!

When you engage in a program that includes strength training, you will begin to reverse the natural aging process of your muscle deteriorating to fat. This process will increase your resting or sedentary metabolism and allow you to burn more calories watching the TV or reading a book. In fact, there are studies that tell us that a strength workout is more important to weight loss than aerobic exercise.

When you do aerobic exercise, your metabolism dramatically increases during the duration of the exercise and remains at the higher lever for an hour or two following the workout. When you engage in a strength workout, your metabolism increases some, but not to the extent of an aerobic workout. The research tells us, though, that our metabolism remains at the higher level for twenty-four to forty-eight hours following the workout. In fact, the research tells us over the workout and the hours that follow, most people will burn more calories by doing a weight workout than by doing an aerobic workout!

When developing your strength workouts, some items to consider are as follow:

- Exercises: As you develop your strength program, find six to eight exercises that work on the large muscle groups of the body. These include the biceps, forearms, chest, triceps, shoulders, back, thighs, buttocks, calves, and abdominal muscles. One of the best resources available for strength training is a book titled *Lean Bodies Total Fitness* by Cliff Sheats. In this book, there are numerous exercises for the muscle groups and good descriptions of how to do each.

▶ Weights: The weights you use should be light enough for you to perform fifteen repetitions of each exercise. The important thing is not how heavy the weight is, but that you can complete fifteen repetitions of each. The ultimate goal is to work up to three sets of fifteen repetitions per exercise. Until you can perform three sets of fifteen repetitions of each exercise, you have no business adding weight to your program. My own program, one which has been in place for five years, still has me lifting only five and ten pound dumbbells for five of my six exercises. This workout is scheduled on the Wednesday, Friday, and Sunday mornings, just before a light run or in the evening. The weight workout takes me less than thirty minutes to complete and has not interfered with my running in the least. The one benefit has been I no longer look like the emaciated runners most associate with distance running today, though I am not anywhere near to entering the Mr. Universe contest!

▶ Motion: The benefit of lifting weights comes from

slow, deliberate motions on each exercise. If you are lifting too much weight, your motion will be affected. The muscle needs to be worked in order to grow, and it is worked better via slow, deliberate motions. If you find your form deteriorating during your workout, you are probably lifting too much weight. Reduce it to an amount you can lift with good form in a slow motion for fifteen repetitions.

▶ The principle of hard/easy applies with weight training, but how it applies is for you take a day off after working a particular muscle group.

Flexibility or Stretching

Again, this is a realm of training which was learned the hard way in my case. (Get the idea I am one of those who learn little without it being the hard way?) When my body began to experience problems from my training regimen, it was suggested that stretching be added to help offset some of the problems. But stretching done improperly and at the wrong time is damaging instead of helpful.

Before we get too far into flexibility, let's look at the benefits of stretching. As we get older, our muscles become shorter and more brittle. Light stretching exercises have proven to offset some of this aging process. In fact, keeping your muscles loose and lengthened will actually help offset some of the ravages of osteoporosis.

Much of my own stretching comes from yoga exercises learned over the years. I do six stretches that are all involving my legs and lower back. Because I have tendon problems where my hamstring connects to my bottom, I have learned to lay on my back while stretching my legs in the air. This keeps pressure off this tendon, something which alleviates much of the pain that is in my hamstring.

Stretching has more to do with the joints and range of motion of the joints than muscles. When you begin to stretch, the key is to move the stretch into a position until you feel tension. Once you feel tension, you will want to hold the stretch for twenty to thirty seconds. My wife was commenting the other night how high school, college, and even professional athletes don't stretch properly as you see them on the sidelines or during their warm up, bouncing in their stretches. This is the worst thing you can do with regard to stretching.

One of the other things not commonly known is stretching is much better done following your exercise than before. Proper warm-up is more important before beginning your exercise than stretching cold muscles. The best way to warm up is by doing the exercise you are beginning to engage in slowly for five to seven minutes. Following this, you may stretch lightly as your muscles have begun to warm up. (My warm-up is usually walking for a half mile before I stretch at all.) Cooling down is also an important aspect of training. Following my runs, the last ten to fifteen minutes are at an easy pace, allowing my heart rate to reduce naturally while still running. When I return from my runs, I do my stretching exercises. This cool down helps my body recover from the workout and prepares me for the next day's workout.

The best advice I can give you with regard to details of stretching is make it specific to the exercise you are doing. Read books on the sport, talk with a physical therapist or exercise physiologist, even people who are proficient in the sport about what stretches are appropriate. Don't just get the body position, try to ascertain what is the goal of the stretch. What muscle group is the stretch isolating?

After acquiring these details, try them out and see how they work for you. Don't be afraid to change how you do it. Just remember to move the muscle to the point where you feel tension, not pain, and hold it there for twenty to thirty seconds. You will find your stretching routine will become defined over the first thirty to sixty days of doing it. The stretches you enjoy and find of benefit will remain, and all the others will disappear.

Developing a structured exercise routine will not only help you feel better about yourself while you're getting your body back to its intended use, but you will find that the activity will allow you to ***Let It Go, Just Let It Go!***

Let It Go—Just Let It Go!

About the Author

Kent Rader is a professional speaker and author who champions the belief that developing happier, healthier employees can lead to success for any organization. Uniquely incorporated with humor, Kent's programs draw upon his management experience as C.E.O./C.F.O. of healthcare organizations, his physical training as a life-long, competitive runner, and his wife's experience as a public school art teacher. A wealth of information is offered in an entertaining environment. Healthy and happy employees contribute to success via employee retention, improved performance and creative problem-solving skills. He has presented programs throughout the United States to organizations wanting to make a positive difference in the lives of those they serve.

Kent A. Rader
Kent Rader Speaks
405-209-3273
kent@kentraderspeaks.com

Let It Go—Just Let It Go!